Survey Your Home for

Structural Building Defects

for Homeowners, Property Developers, Students, Professionals and Property Purchasers

Chris Jenner

Copyright

First Edition 2012
Second Edition 2015
Third Edition 2023

www.HELLOBOOKS.co.uk
HELLO@HELLOBOOKS.co.uk

Dedicated to Nicky *still my inspiration!*

Contents

Introduction

This third edition has been updated with new photographs, tips and general advice to provide the homeowner, property developer, student, professional and property purchaser with a quick and easy reference guide, to identify some of the more common structural building defects found in traditionally built residential properties.

The book includes a comprehensive structural inspection checklist which has been referenced to the structural building defects section. The inspection checklist will direct the reader to the key elements of the building structure to inspect, whilst the structural building defects section includes general advice on what to look out for, why it has happened and what to do now.

A new section has been introduced with case files providing real life context to help the reader understand how to diagnose a building defect, take the appropriate action, obtain sufficient evidence and confidently specify suitable remedial work.

Limitations

This book has been developed by consolidating my many years of structural engineering experience in carrying out inspections and specifying repair works for structural defects found in residential properties. However, diagnosis of structural defects can be complex, as every building is individual in character and many factors can contribute to defects identified.

'This book should not replace the services provided by a qualified professional and should not form the basis to specify, undertake repairs or recommend remedial solutions.'

This book aims to provide guidance to identify structural defects found in residential properties. It does not deal with issues or problems associated with building aesthetics, building fabric, services, thermal or acoustic comfort, medium, high rise or special structures. Special structures can include residential properties built using non-traditional construction techniques (sometimes local to the geographical area) or buildings often referred to as 'system built'. Defects found in this type of property usually require the advice of a professional, as building standards and workmanship are different to that which can be found in traditionally constructed properties and are likely to be outside the scope of this book.

Acknowledgements

Thanks to everyone who has shown an interest and purchased a copy of the book. Thanks to my family, friends, former colleagues, current and previous employers for their support, guidance and for giving me interesting and varied work, without which this book would not have been possible.

In addition, I would like to acknowledge the work of the BRE (Building Research Establishment) as they provide the construction industry with an invaluable information source.

I hope that you will find this book helpful with your initial building assessment.

Photograph left showing a scaffold structure which was designed to provide a temporary buttress support to an old Victorian stone-built structure located in an elevated exposed location. The side wall suffered a partial collapse during a storm, due to inadequate wall restraint, combined with the deterioration of existing building materials.

Chris Jenner is a Chartered Structural Engineer who has been working in the construction industry for over 35 years. Responsible for carrying out structural inspections, identifying building defects, specifying remedial works and for the structural design to a range of low, medium and high-rise properties.

Definitions

Structural Engineering - Is the science and art of designing and making, with economy and elegance, buildings, bridges, frameworks and other similar structures so that they can safely resist the forces to which they may be subjected.
Definition by the Institution of Structural Engineers - www.istructe.org

Structural Element - Any external or internal component of the building which is load-bearing and essential to the overall stability of the building or any part of it.

Principal Structural Elements - Load bearing components of the building, which if defective could affect the **overall** stability of the structure such as roofs, walls, floors, columns, beams and foundations.

Structural Defects - Any defect in a structural element of a building caused by poor workmanship, poor design, deterioration, neglect, abuse, defective materials (or a combination of these) sometimes preventing the continued practical use of the building or part of the building.

Loading - The force or combination of forces that act upon the structure or individual structural elements applied in a vertical or horizontal direction. The forces usually associated and applied to a residential property comprise dead loads (self-weight of materials), imposed loads (non-permanent loads such as snow, furniture, people movements) and wind loads.

Load Path - The route which the forces travel safely through the building, down to foundation level.

Traditional Building Materials - Traditional building materials used in the construction of residential properties and referred to in this book would usually comprise building materials such as masonry walls (brick, block and stone), timber roofs and floors, concrete floor slabs and mass concrete foundations.

Subsidence – The downward vertical movement of the ground which is not due to the weight of the building but due to the loss of support from the soil (See also Settlement). Two common external factors which can cause foundation subsidence are trees and drains (See BD13). Less common are other causes, such as mining subsidence or degradation/consolidation of organic/landfill material.

Settlement – Usually describes initial ground movement due to the weight of a new building or additional loads placed onto an existing building. This type of movement is not usually progressive or severe.

Typical section through a traditionally constructed residential property *Showing the principal structural building elements, loading and load paths.*

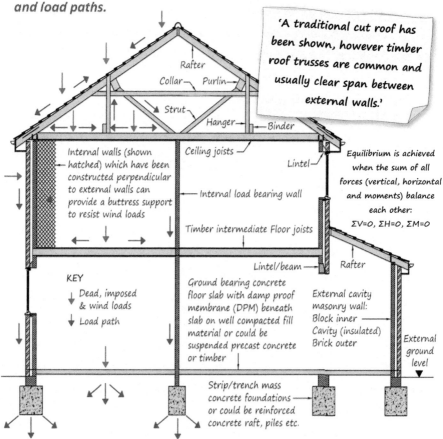

'A traditional cut roof has been shown, however timber roof trusses are common and usually clear span between external walls.'

Rafter

Collar — Purlin —

Strut —

Hanger — — Binder

Internal walls (shown hatched) which have been constructed perpendicular to external walls can provide a buttress support to resist wind loads

Ceiling joists —

Lintel —

Internal load bearing wall

Timber intermediate Floor joists

Equilibrium is achieved when the sum of all forces (vertical, horizontal and moments) balance each other:
$\Sigma V=0, \Sigma H=0, \Sigma M=0$

KEY

↓ Dead, imposed & wind loads

↓ Load path

Lintel/beam —

Rafter

Ground bearing concrete floor slab with damp proof membrane (DPM) beneath slab on well compacted fill material or could be suspended precast concrete or timber

External cavity masonry wall:
Block inner ——
Cavity (insulated)
Brick outer

External ground level

Strip/trench mass concrete foundations —— or could be reinforced concrete raft, piles etc.

Common Types of Professional Inspections and Reports by Qualified Experts

Mortgage valuation inspection & report
usually prepared by a Valuer

This inspection and report is usually requested by a lender to establish the value of the property (at a particular point in time), to determine whether the monies to be lent will comply with the terms and conditions of the loan amount offered and secured against the property. The inspection involves a visual assessment of the exterior/interior of the property and is not intended to be a detailed report. Should major defects be noted, the Valuer may call for a specialist structural inspection and report, to determine the cause of the damage before approving a loan.

Building survey & report usually prepared by a Structural Engineer or Building Surveyor

This survey and report is usually prepared in addition to a mortgage valuation report. It comprises a detailed account of the property. It does not usually include any intrusive investigation, such as opening up the structure by removing the building finishes or fabric or inspecting the condition of the foundations or soil beneath. The client can tailor this inspection and report to suit their needs, which can include the testing of services such as gas, water and electric (usually carried out by specialist tradesman for an additional charge), or by extending the inspection to include outbuildings. The professional fee for this type of report will vary depending upon the amount of detail required and the size, complexity, age of the property.

Homebuyer's survey & valuation report
usually prepared by a Building Surveyor

This survey and report provides information on the general condition of the property and highlights areas which may need attention before making a legal commitment to buy. The report is laid out in a standard format, which does not go into the sort of detail expected from a building survey. It is, however, a more detailed report than that, which is required for a mortgage valuation.

Structural inspection & report
usually prepared by a Structural Engineer

This type of report is usually recommended in a mortgage valuation or homebuyer's survey and valuation report, if structural defects are found. Usually, the type of defect noted will involve cracking to the structure, distortions and signs of structural instability or weakness, which may be cause for concern and which may require further investigation.

Arboricultural inspection & report usually prepared by a qualified Arboriculturalist

This report is usually carried out in conjunction with a Structural Engineers report when vegetation is present, which may be affecting clay soil beneath the foundations, this in turn may be moving and damaging the structure above.

THE STRUCTURAL INSPECTION

Section 1 **The Structural Inspection**

Simplistic Doctors Visit Analogy

 Sometimes it is useful to explain and clarify a process by comparison.

With this in mind, it may be helpful to visualise a building to yourself by thinking of the skeleton as the building structure, the skin as the building finishes/ aesthetics and the internal workings/circulation system as the building services. If this was to be taken one step further, it may be useful to consider the sort of information/questions and procedure that a doctor would follow when assessing a sick patient and how that would relate to a building inspection:

Age, history, vulnerability, location, abuse, how long has it been going on, is it becoming progressively worse, extent of problem, has the cause been previously treated, is immediate action required to stop things getting progressively worse, are further investigations or testing required, are there problems with water works or blockages, extent of medication, monitoring, review, operate!

By considering the above comparison and relating it to the inspection of building defects, it becomes clear that it is important to collect as much evidence as possible and follow a logical trail/sequence before making conclusions and recommendations.

'The Checklist which follows can be used to assist with the initial appraisal/inspection of a building to record the facts, first thoughts and ideas, helping to correctly diagnose any structural building defects which may be found. In addition, sketches are a useful aid to record the pattern, location, extent and magnitude of damaged or deteriorated areas.'

Section A Research, Investigation & Inspection of the Site & the Surrounding Area

A1 Online Services

A2 Archive Information

A3 Public Utilities

A4 Environment Agency & Flood Risk

A5 British Geological Survey

A6 Mining

A7 Property Age

A8 Environment

A9 Seasonal Variations & Weather Conditions

A10 Landscape

A11 Trees

A12 Drainage

A13 The Surrounding Area & Neighbouring Property

Section B Inspection of the Building Structure

B1 Building Type

B2 Building Extensions & Projections

B3 Roofs & Chimneys

B4 Walls

B5 Wall Construction

B6 Wall Construction Material

B7 Foundations

B8 Floors & Ceilings

B9 Structural Alterations

B10 Building Maintenance

B11 Recent Repairs & Decoration

B12 Moisture & Insect Damage

B13 Concrete

'Bringing together all the facts into one place and looking at the information (as a whole), will usually provide a good basis and a logical way for diagnosing the likely cause of any structural defects noted, which will give confidence when specifying useful further investigations and suitable remedial work.'

Section A Research, Investigation & Inspection of the Site & the Surrounding Area

> 'This section includes desk study resources and an inspection of the site and surrounding area to assist with the diagnosis of structural defects found during the inspection of the building.'

A1 Online Services

Visit online mapping websites such as **www.google.co.uk**/maps to establish the site location, surrounding area, environment, site levels and orientation of the building elevations.

Google Earth Pro includes a useful historic imagery tool where the user can view historic aerial photographs showing previous land use and removed features such as building structures, trees and vegetation.

Visit **www.landmark.co.uk** or **www.groundsure.com** to purchase historic maps showing previous land use/records of bomb damage and reports which include information relating to the risk of site hazards associated with the ground conditions, including shrinkable soils, landfill, mining, collapsible ground, landslip/ground instability etc.

A2 Archive Information

Contact the local authority to view or request archive information for the site and surrounding area, including obtaining information relating to areas of known land instability and previous planning applications (which can be viewed by searching the register of planning decisions online at **www.gov.uk**).

> 'Building regulation approval will apply to structural alteration & extension.'

A3 Public Utilities

Contact local public utilities to establish whether **main** underground services travel across or close to the site such as underground foul water (dirty water) and/or surface water systems or gas pipes, water pipes and electric cables.

'Restrictions are in place when building close to main underground services.'

A4 Environment Agency & Flood Risk

'An essential check when purchasing a new property.'

Contact the Environment Agency or visit their website **www.environment-agency.gov.uk** to determine the level of flood risk for the area from nearby rivers, watercourses and tidal areas.

Carry out a local site flood risk assessment by establishing the surrounding ground levels and considering whether the property is susceptible to flooding, due to surface water run off during heavy rain or inclement weather.

A5 British Geological Survey

Geology maps can be viewed or purchased from the British Geological Survey **www.bgs.ac.uk**. These maps indicate the type of natural soil likely to be encountered beneath a site. Maps are usually provided at a 1:50,000 scale.

'Essential information when assessing foundation movement and subsidence.'

'Place or road names such as Clay Pit Avenue, Quarry Lane, Cliff Road, River View, Oak Tree Way, The Orchards, etc. Can be a good indication of the ground condition, current or previous land use and significant topographical features.'

A6 Mining

Large areas across the UK have been affected by mining activities with coal mining being the most common. For further information on past, present and future coal mining activities visit websites such as **www.groundstability.com** or **www.coal.gov.uk**

A7 Property Age

Old buildings have character, including period features. They are rewarding when refurbished to a good standard. But their condition can be costly to maintain, due to general deterioration of building materials with age.

1714 - 1812 Georgian

1812 - 1830 Regency

1830 - 1837 William IV

1837 - 1901 Victorian

1901 - 1910 Edwardian

Old buildings were built using materials, methods and techniques available at the time of construction which are different to current building regulations and/or standards (which have evolved over a period of many years).

1910 - 1936 George V

1936 - 1936 Edward VIII

1936 - 1952 George VI

1952 - 2022 Elizabeth II

2022 to date Charles III

Old buildings may be constructed onto shallow weak foundations, with solid external walls and simple ground bearing floor slabs (which can be susceptible to moisture penetration).

Very old buildings were often built using lime mortars, with internal walls finished using lime plaster, which can be tolerant of minor building movements without cracking.

New buildings have not yet stood the test of time. Defects can manifest shortly after construction with common causes attributed to poor workmanship, poor design and the drying out of materials.

'Significant progressive or re-occurring cracks or defects in old and new homes should be reported to the warranty/insurance provider or to a qualified professional (as applicable) as soon as identified for further inspection and investigation.'

Initial foundation settlement in newly constructed homes (not to be confused with subsidence) can occur up to approximately five years after construction.

Foundation settlement can cause cracking which should not be progressive and can be easily repaired and redecorated.

New homes are likely to be covered by a ten-year insurance backed warranty.

A8 Environment

Consider environmental conditions which can cause premature deterioration of building materials, such as industrial environments, marine environments (salt water), or sites on exposed or in high altitude locations, which can intensify wind, rain and temperature variations (with the greatest temperature changes usually occurring on south facing elevations).

'PHOTO SHOWING A BUILDING STRUCTURE CONSTRUCTED ONTO A CLIFF TOP LOCATED IN AN EXTREME EXPOSED ENVIRONMENT.'

A9 Seasonal Variations & Weather Conditions

Inspecting homes at different times of the year and during different weather conditions can be useful. Defects such as condensation, water penetration and boggy ground conditions, may be easily identifiable during the winter months. Whilst ground surface cracks, during prolonged dry periods in the summer months, could be an indication of shrinkable clay soils.

SEE BD13. 2.1.1

A10 Landscape

Inspect the direction and gradient of slopes including their proximity to the building structure. Consider also the proximity of ditches, cliffs and areas of known land instability, all of which could affect ground stability.

Homes which have been constructed onto the top of slopes can be at a 'higher' risk of foundation movement as sloping ground (particularly steeper slopes) tends to move with gravity from the top to the bottom. The cause of such movement can be complex and will depend on the ground conditions, the presence of ground water and external factors.

External factors can include erosion, surcharge loading, leaking drainage pipes and tree removal.

'PHOTO SHOWING LANDSLIP CAUSED BY MOVEMENT OF NEARBY STEEPLY SLOPING GROUND.'

Identify retaining walls (constructed to cater for differences in the ground level) and assess their age and condition.

SEE BD12

Consider whether there is a possibility that the site has been filled to make it level, by review of old maps and topography of the site/area.

A11 Trees

Record and note the condition of any trees located on the site or close to the site boundary including tree type, height, distance from the building, proximity to underground drainage pipes and risk of falling onto structures.

SEE BD14

NATIONAL HOUSE BUILDING COUNCIL (NHBC) STANDARDS

NHBC Standards chapter 4.2 provides simple guidance for building near trees on sites with slopes not exceeding 1 in 7. This chapter aims to deal with the hazards associated with foundations constructed in **shrinkable clays** with existing or removed trees nearby.

Tables and charts are used to determine foundation depths up to 2.50m below ground level, including the requirement for ground heave precautions.

The interaction between buildings, trees and clay soils is complex and it should be noted that the guidance given in this chapter is intended to provide an acceptable risk level that the foundation will not experience a damaging amount of movement for NHBC warranty acceptance.

As a rough guide, a building should not be constructed on shallow foundations in a clay soil closer than a single trees mature height, increasing to one and half times the mature height for groups of trees. It should be noted that the tree species is a key factor as the ground water demand and root system will vary between broad leaf and coniferous trees. Some willow trees have a very high water demand with a wide root system which can spread out to two times the height of the tree.

A12 Drainage

'Underground drain failure is a common cause of foundation subsidence. Drains can become damaged or defective due to tree roots, ground movements, landslip, traffic overloading, design life exceeded or by poor construction techniques such as the provision of inadequate movement joints.'

SEE BD13

▸ Turn on taps and flush toilets to see how the water drains away.

▸ Lift manholes to check the type and condition of pipes, concrete benching (the smooth render in the base of the manhole) and evidence of whether the water level significantly rises above the pipe invert (the level inside the bottom of the pipe), which could indicate an undersized pipe, a regular blockage or a defective or overloaded system.

Cracks or splits in the pipes or in the concrete benching, could indicate defects or a leaking pipe, which could be washing out or softening soils, possibly beneath nearby foundations.

▸ Insufficient or lack of manholes and inspection chambers will make accessing the system difficult and costly should the underground pipes become blocked.

'Ideally, underground drainage pipes should be located at shallower depths than adjacent foundations to avoid undermining during construction and/or repair work and to reduce the risk of damage to foundations caused by a leaking drainage pipe.

It is possible that foundation damage can occur due to the consolidation of weak backfill material should the sides of a drainage trench become surcharged (loaded) by foundations.'

▸ Check the condition of surface water gutters and downpipes (check behind downpipes for damp patches on walls). Inspect when it is raining or use a hose pipe to test the system for leaks or damp patches on walls.

▶ Beware of missing sections of gutter and surface water downpipes discharging directly onto or into the ground, which can cause dampness to walls and/or wash out or soften soils beneath shallow foundations.

'Reinstatements in paths along the drainage runs can indicate recent repairs or previous investigation work.'

▶ Consider whether the foul drainage system (dirty water) discharges into the main sewer, cesspit or to a septic tank and whether the surface water discharges into the main sewer system, a nearby water course, ditch or into a soakaway (which should be placed at a minimum of 5m away from a building foundation).

A13 The Surrounding Area & Neighbouring Property

▶ Inspect similar neighbouring buildings for comparable defects which could indicate poorly designed or constructed details, poor workmanship, choice of wrong materials or widespread problems with the ground beneath foundations.

▶ Inspect the surrounding area for unstable slopes, unusual changes in level, the ground surface for cracks and hard paved areas for cracks or movements, which may indicate ground instability.

▶ Inspect the condition of freestanding and boundary walls.

SEE BD12

▶ Consider the risk of vibration caused by nearby airports, heavily trafficked roads and railway lines.

▶ Consider the proximity of the building to major construction works such as deep foundations, wells, shafts & tunnels, which could affect the stability of the surrounding ground.

'PHOTO RIGHT SHOWING AN OLD BRICK-BUILT GARDEN WELL, LOCATED APPROXIMATELY 1M AWAY FROM THE BUILDING STRUCTURE. THE WELL WAS SUBSEQUENTLY INVESTIGATED AND FILLED IN.'

Section B Inspection of the Building Structure

 'This section relates to the visual inspection of the structural building elements and construction details.'

B1 Building Type (detached, semi-detached, mid terrace, end terrace, maisonettes, flats, bungalows etc.)

Building structures should be inspected and considered as a whole, particularly when attached to an adjoining property or in the case of flats. Works or damage to adjacent buildings can have an adverse effect on the adjoining property, which may show signs of similar defects.

B2 Building Extensions & Projections

'Bay Windows Garages, Porches Extensions Conservatories. etc.'

Consider the type, location, and construction date of building additions. Check the quality of the workmanship, materials and investigate with the local authority or owner whether the structure was constructed in accordance with building regulations and/or planning approval and if so, are any plans or details available.

Inspect the junction between any building addition and/or projection and the building structure, as this can be a weak point and movement or a crack at this location may highlight a potential problem. Potential causes can include foundation subsidence or differential foundation settlements and/or movements (particularly if the foundations are located at different depths bearing onto different soil types/ strengths). It is common for a vertical movement joint to be constructed at this location as an alternative to bonded or toothed masonry (which can be susceptible to cracking and movement).

SEE BD13

> 'SOME CONSERVATORIES DO NOT NEED TO COMPLY WITH THE CURRENT BUILDING REGULATIONS. THE QUALITY OF WORKMANSHIP AND MATERIALS CAN VARY, INCLUDING THE PROVISION OF A SUITABLE FOUNDATION AND FLOOR CONSTRUCTION.'

B3 Roofs & Chimneys

Inspect the roof from the outside by standing away from the building and by holding a straight edge at arm's length such as a spirit level along the line of the **SEE BD1 TO BD3** ridge (apex of the roof) and hips (sloping corners) to check for line and level. Use binoculars to gain a close-up view of the roof and chimney from the ground level. Where possible secure a long ladder against the wall for a close up examination of the condition of the roof covering and to detect unevenness in the roof slopes.

Inspect the roof structure from within the loft space and note that all timbers used in a traditional cut roof should be accurately positioned.

The main timber components in a traditional cut roof comprise: Rafters which carry the weight of the roof finishes; ceiling joists (often referred to as ceiling ties) which triangulate the rafters, stop the walls/roof from moving outwards and are used for supporting the ceiling finishes/loft storage.

Binders and hangers are used to support long spanning ceiling joists and the ridge board provides a fixing point for the top of the rafters to suit rafter spacing. Purlins provide support to long rafter spans, stiffen the structure, and can be supported by timber struts which transfer the load onto the structure below. Collars (horizontal members at purlin positions) can be used to tie large roofs together. Purlins and binders should be built into the supporting structure where possible.

'PHOTO SHOWING AN OLD SAGGING ROOF, WHICH HAD TO BE MADE SAFE.'

In valley and hipped roofs, the hip and valley rafters carry loads from two sections of the roof and sometimes require intermediate support. See also drawing section in definitions and BD2

'Be cautious when inspecting tall and slender chimney stacks as they can easily become unstable due to defects or out of balance loads.'

Check that the internal chimney breast is continuous through the building. It is common to find the breast removed at ground or first floors without providing adequate support to the chimney stack above, resulting in a potential out of balance, unstable load at high level.

'NEW LINTELS RE-SUPPORTING A CHIMNEY STACK.'

B4 **Walls**

▸ Check walls for cracking and for movement by standing at one corner and looking along the line of the wall to view the far corner, using the line of the mortar joints, window sills and window reveals as a reference. In addition, a long spirit level or a plumb line could be placed up against the wall to check for line and level.

▸ Look out of windows for bowing or bulging walls and to inspect the condition of the wall and lintels or arches over openings. See BD9

▸ Check whether windows/doors open freely and for frame distortion.

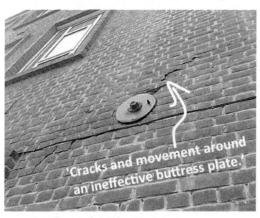

'Cracks and movement around an ineffective buttress plate.'

◀ Check for wall buttress plates such as steel channels, disc or 'S' plates which have been used to provide restraint to the walls. These plates indicate previous problems with the walls and they should be carefully assessed for their effectiveness. See BD9

▸ Check all internal wall junctions, room by room for signs of cracking and movement (floor/wall, wall/wall, wall/ceiling).

▸ Check the condition of internal walls beneath concentrated loads such as roof struts and beam bearings.

▸ Measure the size of any cracks for future reference by using the crack measurement guide in BD5 and try to determine the age of the cracks. Newer cracks will appear clean with sharp edges.

B5 Wall Construction

'Timber Frame
Cavity Wall
Single Skin
Solid Wall
Combination?'

Identify the wall construction and be aware that there are many different types of construction in use, including 'system built' properties and specially constructed properties using materials and techniques local to the geographical area. Defects found in these special types of property usually require professional advice, as building standards and workmanship can be different than that found in traditionally constructed properties.

Historically, masonry walls were constructed using individual units laid in patterns, usually referred to as the wall bond. The bond of a wall will influence its strength due to differences on how the individual units are tied or restrained together. As a guide the horizontal centres of the vertical joints (perpends) should not be positioned less than one quarter of the length of the masonry unit in the adjacent course.

Solid walls can be built using brick, block, or stone with a total thickness of up to 500mm (particularly in solid stone walls). 225mm thick solid brick walls can be recognised by the pattern of the brickwork, whereby the bricks are usually placed both head on and lengthways. 100mm solid walls can usually be identified by examining their thickness at window reveals or door openings.

'SOLID WALLS ARE VULNERABLE TO MOISTURE PENETRATION AND CAN BE STRUCTURALLY WEAK DEPENDING ON THEIR CONDITION, THICKNESS, AND RESTRAINT.'

Cavity walls can be built using a combination of brickwork or concrete blocks with a total thickness of approximately 300mm. Note that the wall thickness in newer homes is generally increasing to allow for a greater thickness of cavity wall insulation to comply with current regulations. Bricks are usually placed lengthways in pattern, separated with a cavity (sometimes insulated). The two skins of masonry are fixed together using wall ties (located in panels at approximately 900mm horizontal and 450mm vertical centres).

Wall ties in older properties are prone to deterioration.

SEE BD10

Be aware that the inappropriate specification of retrospectively installed wall insulation injected through small holes into the cavity of older properties can increase the risk of damage to the building materials. Cavity wall insulation can reduce air flow and can prevent the drying out of building materials resulting in the facing masonry skin being colder and wetter for longer,

'PHOTO SHOWING SMALL HOLES IN AN EXTERNAL WALL WHERE INSULATION HAS BEEN RETROSPECTIVELY INSTALLED.'

increasing the risk of water penetration and frost damage. Note that inappropriate use of silicone wall treatments can lock in moisture and stop the drying out of the masonry, increasing the risk of frost damage.

> 'Inspect and test the condition of the bricks below the damp proof course at ground level (particularly in exposed locations) by using the point of a sharp tool to establish whether the surface is hard. If the bricks are soft or start flaking (fragments breaking away from the brick face) further investigation may be required to confirm the structural adequacy of the bricks.'

B6 Wall Construction Material

Natural Stone See BD 6.1 **Brick** See BD 6.2 **Concrete Block and Artificial Stone Blocks** See BD 6.3

Wall Cladding (slates, tiles, boarding, render, plastic panels etc.)

When inspecting a wall which has been clad, it is necessary to understand why the wall has been covered up. Wall cladding can be used as weather protection for single skin walls or can conceal damaged, cracked or weak masonry walls. Be aware that there are certain forms of cladding which give the appearance of brickwork such as mathematical tiles and to assist with their identification, check corner junctions for vertical un-bonded joints or for a change in wall construction.

B7 Foundations

Consider the type and condition of the existing foundations. It is likely that older properties will have shallow foundations, whilst new properties, additions or extensions (which have been built to conform to newer building regulations) are likely to have been constructed with deeper foundations.

Differential foundation settlements and/or movements can occur when different parts of a building have been constructed onto different depth foundation types and/or at different foundation depths.

 SEE BD13

Ground investigations and hand dug trial holes (usually specified by the Engineer and carried out by an experienced contractor) can be carried out to inspect the condition of the foundations and the soil beneath, including checking for the presence of roots, soft soils, fill material and the height of the water table.

'Look out for reinstatements in paths adjacent to the building, which could indicate that previous trial hole investigations have been carried out, particularly in areas close to visible structural damage such as new or repaired wall cracks and movements.'

B8 Floors & Ceilings

Determine the type of floor

 SEE BD16

construction and walk all the floors checking the floor/wall junctions and ceiling/wall junctions for signs of movement.

'To determine the presence of a sloping or uneven floor, place a small ball (marble) on a hard floor or use a spirit level.'

Note that timber defects are likely in suspended timber ground floors if the damp proof course (DPC) is no longer effective or if the vents (commonly referred to as air bricks) are blocked or have not been provided. In this case a new DPC or provision of ventilation may be advisable even where there are no signs of visible damage.

Inspect the ceilings and be aware that original ceilings in older buildings can be constructed using lath and plaster, whereas ceilings in newer buildings comprise mainly of plasterboard. Ceiling cracks/distortions can indicate defects with the supporting structure.

Old lath and plaster ceilings are brittle and the plaster can de-bond from the timber laths causing localised failures.

Cracking/distortion of plasterboard ceilings can occur where boards are not fixed in a staggered pattern, if boards are not strong enough to span between supports, inadequate support at board edges and/or poorly constructed joints.

'PHOTO ABOVE SHOWING A BRITTLE FAILURE OF AN OLD LATH AND PLASTER CEILING.'

B9 Structural Alterations

Look out for alterations, such as the removal of a load bearing wall to create an open plan area.

Be cautious when planning a structural alteration and be aware that timber studwork walls can be loadbearing and can provide stability to the existing structure.

The structural function of all walls should be properly investigated before demolition.

'Photo above showing a braced loadbearing timber stud-work wall (finishes removed), which was made unstable when a diagonal brace was cut to create a new door opening.'

SEE BD24

B10 Building Maintenance

If a building has been left vacant, un-heated or un-ventilated for a long period of time, without carrying out any routine maintenance, it is likely that defects will exist and repair work will be required. See section 3

B11 Recent Repairs & Decoration

Look for recent repairs, refurbishment or decoration works and consider whether it is an attempt to cover up building defects. Enquire with the existing building owner (if appropriate) whether any defects were found during any such works. Check for poor workmanship, which could indicate the level of care and quality of any repair work undertaken.

SEE BD27

> **'Beware of dry lining of walls (whereby gaps are left between the wall finishes & wall making a hollow sound when tapped) which could cover up a potential damp problem, can be an easy way of disguising or covering up a defect or may have been used to provide a flat surface to an uneven wall.'**

B12 Moisture & Insect Damage

Locate the external damp proof course, inspect it for type/general condition and that it has not been covered over by a raised ground level adjacent to the wall of the building or bridged by render or mortar. Try to determine (from the existing building owner if appropriate) whether there has been a previous history of damp penetration through walls and floors and, if so, have repair works been successful, what were they, and are there any contractors guarantees. Smell for signs of hidden timber

SEE BD20 TO BD23

rot and tap timber members to help identify areas of rot. Decayed timber will produce a dull sound, whilst a structurally sound timber member will sound solid and have a ring to it. Buckling skirting boards can indicate high levels of moisture in the wall.

B13 Concrete

Identify structural concrete elements and assess their condition.

SEE BD19

CHECKLIST SUMMARY - YOUR NOTES

For use when carrying out the initial building assessment with notes recorded against each item together with sketches prepared separately (where applicable).

A1   Online Services:

A2   Archive Information:

A3   Public Utilities:

A4   Environment Agency & Flood Risk:

A5   British Geological Survey:

A6   Mining:

A7   Property Age:

A8   Environment:

A9   Seasonal Variations & Weather Conditions:

A10   Landscape:

A11   Trees:

A12   Drainage:

A13   The Surrounding Area & Neighbouring Property:

B1   Building Type:

B2   Building Extensions & Projections:

B3   Roofs and Chimneys:

B4   Walls:

B5   Wall Construction:

B6   Wall Construction Material:

B7   Foundations:

B8   Floors & Ceilings:

B9   Structural Alterations:

B10   Building Maintenance:

B11   Recent Repairs & Decoration:

B12   Moisture & Insect Damage:

B13   Concrete:

Section 2 Structural Building Defects

'THIS SECTION PROVIDES A QUICK AND EASY REFERENCE GUIDE TO SOME OF THE MORE COMMON STRUCTURAL DEFECTS FOUND IN RESIDENTIAL PROPERTIES.'

BD1 Roof Defects

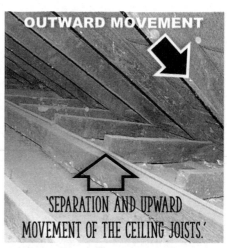

OUTWARD MOVEMENT

'SEPARATION AND UPWARD MOVEMENT OF THE CEILING JOISTS.'

1.1 Roof Spread in pitched roofs (cut and assembled on site).

1.1.1 What to look out for

Deformation of the roof profile at the ridge or on the slope, walls bowing/cracks appearing at eaves level (the lower edge of the roof), usually travelling in a horizontal direction and in one or more of the top courses of masonry, combined with the roof line moving in an outwards direction.

'Photo above showing roof spread caused by inadequate restraint of the rafter at the support position.'

1.1.2 Why has it happened

If the roof rafters are weak, have been poorly designed and/or inadequately constructed or if they are not triangulated with or fixed to the ceiling joists, they can move in an outward direction at their support position, particularly if the support is an unrestrained masonry wall.

1.1.3 What to do now

Depending upon the roof configuration (See BD2) roof spread can be stabilised by providing a vertical support to the roof (such as a ridge beam), tying rafter feet back to existing or new structural members, or by strengthening the existing connections or supporting structure.

1.2 Other Roof Defects - What to look out for See also BD1.3

▶ Rotten and deteriorated roof timbers, particularly at the junction with a chimney stack or within an internal box or valley gutter, which could be caused by general deterioration due to age or by a prolonged leaking roof. See BD21

▶ Poor materials and workmanship which can be associated with the original construction or with previous repairs & roof strengthening.

> **'Flat roofs are prone to defects due to the short lifespan of some roof coverings or due to poor workmanship and/or design, including poor falls and drainage which can result in ponding water, which can overload and damage the supporting structure.'**

▶ Inadequately designed or poorly constructed loft conversions and other structural alterations.

▶ Inadequate/insufficient structural members.

▶ Replacement roof coverings being heavier than the original covering (overloading the supporting structure).

▶ Damage from insect attack (usually starting at the joints where the end grain is easily penetrated). See BD23

▶ Overloading and cracking of internal supporting walls (particularly beneath concentrated loads from roof struts).

▶ Overloading of the ceiling joists caused by the storage of heavy items (check for cracks and deflection in the ceiling finishes below).

▶ Unsupported chimney stack removal or inadequate support of water tanks.

▶ Inadequate bracing along the length of the roof and/or restraint of separating/end (gable) walls. See BD1.3

▶ Insulation being placed hard up around the edges of the roof (in cold roof construction), blocking the roof ventilation and increasing the risk of timbers becoming damp from condensation. See BD20

▶ Inadequate pitch of roof to suit roof covering material (tiles/slates) which can increase the chance of snow and rain penetration.

> **'Check whether a fire separation wall has been constructed between joined loft spaces.'**
> See BD 25

1.3 Trussed Rafter Roofs

Fabricated off site and usually craned into position.

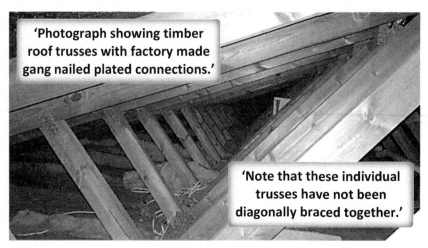

'Photograph showing timber roof trusses with factory made gang nailed plated connections.'

'Note that these individual trusses have not been diagonally braced together.'

1.3.1 What to look out for

▶ Check the horizontal and vertical alignment of the truss by holding a spirit level against individual trusses or visually by looking down the line of several trusses.

▶ As a guide, trusses are usually spaced at 600mm centres (or less) and should be erected within a tolerance of 25mm to the vertical. Performance may be affected if the trusses are outside these guidelines.

▶ Check for adequate support at changes in roof direction, such as doubled up trusses or specially made trusses to support concentrations of load.

'Trussed rafters are used as an economical means of roof framing as standard components are produced using an economic efficient factory process. They are lightweight and can be erected quickly on site, achieving clear spans between 4m – 12m depending upon their arrangement.'

- Check that the trusses have been diagonally braced to prevent their racking (collapse of roof trusses like dominoes). Missing braces should be reinstated as soon as possible.

- Check the condition of the gang nail plated connections (used to fix the timbers together), as failure of this connection will affect the structural integrity of the roof truss.

- Check that the storage of items and the load of heavy items such as water tanks, are evenly spaced over several trusses to prevent overloading individual truss members.

- Ensure that the roof truss is being supported at the correct load point on the timber wall plate (See BD2), as supporting the truss at the wrong location could distort and weaken the timber members.

- Notching, drilling, or cutting of a timber member will weaken the structure causing a potential failure, as the timber members are usually manufactured to their design limit. See BD17

'Structural alterations which are carried out to the roof structure, such as loft conversions, require approval and certification from a building control authority (approved inspector or local authority). Completion certificates should be checked to determine whether any such works have been properly designed and carried out in accordance with the building regulations.'

- Gable and party separating walls should be laterally restrained (tied back) to the timber trusses, using galvanised restraint straps.

- In exposed locations or when a lightweight roof covering material has been used, check that holding down straps have been fixed over the supporting timber wall plate and down the wall.

BD2 Roof Structure Examples

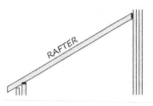

(Limited to spans upto approx 3m)

1) LEAN TO ROOF

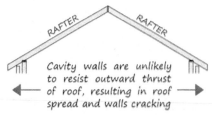

Cavity walls are unlikely to resist outward thrust of roof, resulting in roof spread and walls cracking

2) COUPLE ROOF

Rafter may bend between support and tie resulting in deflection/roof spread and cracking of the supporting walls. The loads onto the end of the rafter will be increased as the tie is raised and the span increased

3) COLLAR / RAISED TIE ROOF

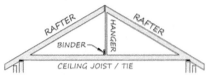

A hanger and binder is introduced to keep ceiling tie/joists to a minimum size, used when spans exceed approx 2.5m with the roof arrangement usually limited to spans up to approx 5.5m

4) CLOSE COUPLE ROOF

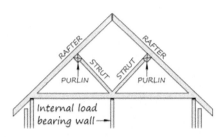

Purlins are introduced for spans in excess of 6m to keep rafter size to a minimum

5) STRUTTED PURLIN ROOF

Roof trusses usually clear span between external walls and are constructed from smaller timber members using special gang nailed plated connections

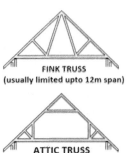

FINK TRUSS
(usually limited upto 12m span)

ATTIC TRUSS

6) EXAMPLES OF FACTORY ASSEMBLED ROOF TRUSSES

BD3 Chimneys

3.1 What to look out for

'PHOTO SHOWING A TALL SLENDER CHIMNEY STACK.'

▷ Horizontal and vertical cracking, sometimes combined with twisting and leaning (usually greater than 1mm in 100mm), particularly when associated with tall and slender unrestrained chimney stacks.

▷ Heavy attachments such as aerials, which can affect stability.

▷ Broken or loose chimney pots, which can fall from the structure.

3.2 Why has it happened

▷ Material defects due to deterioration with age are common as chimneys are exposed to extremes of weather, including frost damage caused by freezing and thawing of water.

▷ Sulphates contained within the masonry or mortar (materials) can chemically react with moisture causing expansion of the material, sometimes combined with horizontal cracking (See BD15). Externally the moisture source is likely to be due to wetting caused by rainfall. Chimney stacks which lean towards the south are believed to be affected by this chemical reaction. The south facing side of the chimney is often drier because of exposure to prevailing winds and sun, with the expansion usually taking place to a greater degree on the opposite slow drying side. Internally the moisture source can be due to water vapour contained within flue gasses condensing onto the cold uninsulated surfaces. This moisture can contain weak acids (from the flue gasses) which can accelerate deterioration.

'Be aware that artificial chimney stacks can be found on newer buildings and are used for aesthetic reasons.'

▷ Heat expansion of flue linings can transfer loads to the masonry causing vertical or horizontal cracking.

3.3 What to do now

▶ Check that the stack is stable and if in doubt have it taken down to a safe level to suit its required use or remove it altogether.

▶ Demolish and rebuild the chimney using good quality materials and flue liners.

▶ In some cases, the top of the stack can be restrained using metal straps and steel tie rods, which can be fixed back to roofs, walls or strong points on the building.

'CHECK THAT THE INTERNAL CHIMNEY BREAST IS CONTINUOUS THROUGH THE BUILDING AS IT IS COMMON TO REMOVE THE BREAST AT GROUND OR FIRST FLOOR LEVELS WITHOUT PROVIDING ADEQUATE SUPPORT TO THE CHIMNEY STACK ABOVE, RESULTING IN A POTENTIAL OUT OF BALANCE & UNSTABLE LOAD AT HIGH LEVEL.'

'Chimney stacks can deteriorate earlier than other building elements due to their exposed location. In particular, the waterproof detail at the junction between the roof/chimney and deterioration of the brickwork and mortar joints, which can sometimes allow rainwater to penetrate down into the structure and/or cause structural instability.'

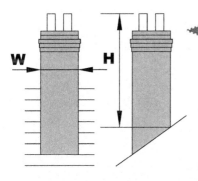

'Newer building regulations recommend that where a chimney is not adequately supported by ties or restrained in any way, its height (H) measured to the top of the chimney pot or flue terminal from the highest junction with the roof surface should not exceed 4.5 x the least horizontal dimension (W) of the chimney.'

BD4 Bay Windows

4.1 What to look out for

Cracking and distortion of the ground and first floor supporting walls particularly at the junctions between the main building and bay structure. Windows can stick in their frames and not open freely.

4.2 Damage caused by replacement windows in fully glazed bay windows

In older properties it is common to find that the original load bearing timber window frames have been replaced with lightweight, non-load-bearing plastic frames without properly designed lintels. These frames are not strong enough to transfer the building loads down to the foundations and can cause the structure and windows to distort and crack. The damage can be made worse if inadequate temporary propping was used during the window replacement works.

4.2.1 What to do now

It would usually be necessary to replace or strengthen the ground and first floor window frames, including the bay window structure between the openings, using properly designed lintels with load bearing structural posts.

'In severe cases, the repair could involve complete reconstruction of the bay window (see photo right).'

4.3 Damage caused by movement/deterioration of timber framing See also BD22

It is common to find that the bay structure has been partly constructed using timber framing. This timber framing can deteriorate, rot or crack and/or move due to differential thermal movements between the different building materials (See BD7) or between the frame and building, if it has not been adequately tied back to the main walls or floors.

4.3.1 What to do now

Repair and/or replace defective timber members and/or tie the timber frame back to the main structure. Cracks could then be repaired or hidden behind a weatherproof cover strip as there is a possibility that they may continue to open and close.

4.4 Damage caused by foundation movement/subsidence

See also BD13

The ground floor wall is usually constructed using masonry and a crack at this level may indicate subsidence or differential foundation settlement, particularly as bay windows are often constructed onto shallower foundations than the main building (see photo right showing cracking and distortion caused by foundation subsidence).

4.4.1 What to do now

A small trial hole could be dug to determine the condition of the existing foundation and soil beneath, as it is possible that the foundation may need to be strengthened (See BD13). Permanent repairs should be postponed until it has been established that the damage is not becoming progressively worse.

BD5 Walls - Crack Measurement Guide

5.1 The cause of any cracks and whether they are getting progressively worse should be established as soon as possible.

It is generally recognised that if an isolated crack is 2mm or less in width and does not vary by more than 1mm over a 12-month period, structural repair is not usually necessary. Should lots of smaller cracks be noted measuring less than 2mm in width there may be cause for concern as this could indicate widespread unpredictable foundation movement (See BD13). Crack effects can appear in a variety of forms including shear, tension, compression, expansion, or rotation. Analysis of the cracking form can be useful to assist with defect diagnosis.

0.20mm

2.00mm

5.00mm

15.00mm

25.00mm

0.10mm or less (insignificant) Hairline cracks which are difficult to see. These cracks are not usually considered to be structurally significant.

0.20mm to 2.00mm (slight - moderate) Fine cracks which are easy to see when approaching 2mm in width. Cracks may have some structural significance but not usually serious.

2.00mm to 5.00mm (moderate) Cracks will be very noticeable when approaching 5mm in width. Cracks are likely to have some structural significance and are likely to have been caused by ground movements.

5.00mm to 15.00mm (moderate - severe) Cracks of this size are usually associated with severe damage especially when approaching 15mm in width. Cracks are likely to affect the structural integrity of the building.

15.00mm to 25.00mm (severe - very severe) Cracks which could affect the structural integrity of the building.

25.00mm or more (very severe - dangerous) Cracks which will have the potential to make the building unsafe.

'For further reading see BRE Digest 251 Assessment of Damage in low rise Structures. This digest discusses the assessment and classification of visible damage resulting from structural distortion.'

BD6 **Wall Materials**

Local wall materials can be specific to the geographical area (common examples have been included):

6.1 **Natural Stone**

Natural stones fit into one of the following three groups classified as either igneous (granite), metamorphic (marble and slate) or sedimentary (limestone, sandstone and chalk). Sedimentary limestone and sandstone rocks have been widely used as a building stone and their strength and durability can vary depending upon their classification and origin.

6.1.1 **What to look out for**

6.1.1.1 **Surface erosion**

Affecting both sandstones and limestones

The rate of weathering, erosion and gradual deterioration can vary depending on exposure condition. Deterioration is inevitable if the surface of the stone is constantly wet from rainwater.

6.1.1.2 **Frost damage**

Mainly affecting limestones

Moisture can penetrate the stone which expands when frozen, causing fragments to break away from the larger stone (referred to as spalling). Worst in exposed areas which are susceptible to excessive moisture and frost but rarely occurring between the damp proof course and roof eaves level. The degree of vulnerability is believed to be related to the porosity of the stone with porous stones being the most vulnerable to damage.

6.1.1.3 **Environmental damage** *(salt crystallisation)*

Affecting both sandstones and limestones

Stones with naturally high levels of salts, salt contaminated sands used for mortars, ground salts and sea spray can damage stones, sometimes appearing as a general powdering of the surface or exfoliating, spalling or shattering. Solids, such as beach sands can abrade the surface when wind-blown.

6.1.1.4 Atmospheric pollution (acid rain)

Affecting both sandstones and limestones

Fragments of stone, which vary in size, can break away from the larger stone, due to sulphur gasses dissolved in rainwater chemically reacting with the stone.

'Old natural stone walls can easily become damaged or unstable if structural alterations are carried out by in-experienced designers and/or contractors.'

'Photo above showing inadequate temporary propping causing cracks to appear in the structure above the props. Photo right showing service penetrations causing cracking and local collapse.'

6.1.1.5 Corrosion of embedded fixings

Affecting both sandstones and limestones

Damage to stones can occur when embedded steel or iron fixings corrode and expand.

6.1.1.6 Stone bedding

Affecting both sandstones and limestones

Premature deterioration and delamination of stone layers can occur when individual stones are not laid on their natural bed (layers should be horizontal). Soft weaker layers can exist in some stones which can deteriorate quicker than the remaining stone.

6.1.1.7 Contour scaling *Affecting sandstones*

Thermal expansion and/or moisture movements between the body of the stone and the surface can cause a crust to break away to a depth of between 5mm-20mm (usually within the wetting depth caused by rainwater).

'Stones should be kept clean from algae and lichen, which can smother the stone and keep it wet for longer, eventually causing pitting or erosion of the surface. Some stones can become fractured and weakened by the extraction process, particularly if professionally mined using explosives.'

6.2 Bricks

The two most widely used types of brick are clay or calcium silicate (less common pale bricks made by a reaction of lime and sand or crushed flint). Clay bricks suitable for general building purposes are described as common. Facing clay bricks are especially made for their attractive appearance and engineering clay bricks have strong compressive strength and a good resistance to frost damage and water penetration. Brickwork defects are common where areas of brickwork remain wet for long periods or due to water penetration. Bricks should ideally be chosen not only for aesthetics, but also for strength and durability, particularly when exposed to extreme weather or temperature variations or where located in vulnerable exposed locations such as chimney stacks, wall parapets, below damp proof courses and in retaining/garden walls. Note that correct material specification does not cater for defects which can arise from sub-standard materials or from poor standards of workmanship.

6.2.1 What to look out for

6.2.1.1 Moisture expansion of clay bricks
Clay bricks can expand soon after they are fired as they absorb atmospheric moisture, which is irreversible. See BD7

'Photo showing vertical cracking due to the omission of external movement joints.'

6.2.1.2 Calcium silicate bricks

Calcium silicate bricks are usually smoother and paler in colour than clay bricks. These bricks have a good resistance to sulphate attack but they are susceptible to movements caused by drying shrinkage. This necessitates a greater allowance for movement by providing joints at approximately 6m centres, which is approximately half the recommended distance for clay bricks. See BD7

6.2.1.3 Frost damage of clay bricks

Moisture in the brick can freeze and expand causing brick fragments to break away from the brick face (referred to as spalling). This damage is likely to occur in older bricks, brickwork below the damp proof course level, wall parapets and in freestanding/retaining walls. In these areas, frost resistance bricks should be used. Frost resistance depends upon the porosity of the brick, with the resistance to attack increasing as the brick becomes less permeable.

'Some bricks are weak and prone to failure. When the face of weak bricks fail, the core can become exposed, which will easily erode (see photo right). This type of failure is difficult to repair, as trying to replace the bricks can often result in making the situation worse and in many cases the best option may be to protect the bricks with cladding or render.

If the masonry is load bearing it should be properly assessed by a Structural Engineer as soon as possible, to help prevent the sudden collapse of badly deteriorated walls.'

6.2.1.4 Firing and efflorescence of clay bricks

If bricks are over fired during the manufacturing process they can be brittle and if under fired they can be weaker (softer) than normal and left with a high level of sulphate (salts). Sulphates present in clay bricks can be brought to the surface by water as walls dry out, crystallising on the surface and appearing as a white deposit called efflorescence. Persistent efflorescence may indicate wet or saturated bricks, possibly caused by a design fault. In most cases efflorescence itself will not affect the strength of a wall but may be an aesthetic concern.

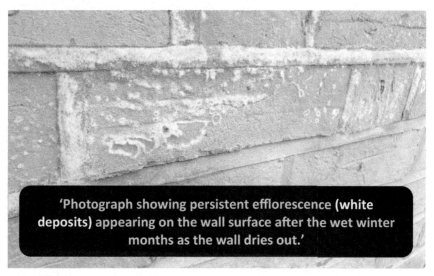

'Photograph showing persistent efflorescence (white deposits) appearing on the wall surface after the wet winter months as the wall dries out.'

6.3 Blocks

Early concrete blocks were crude and mainly used for the construction of internal partitions. This type of block can be brittle as they were manufactured using cement mixed with locally available aggregate such as, industrial waste products including breeze (cinders) and clinker (blast furnace slag).

Concrete blocks began to replace bricks in the construction of the inner skin of a cavity masonry wall as they were cheaper to use, quick to build with and required less skill to lay (one block equalling approximately 6 bricks). Concrete blocks are widely used due to their variety of strength, insulation and sound reducing properties.

6.3.1 Types of concrete block

6.3.1.1 Dense aggregate block

This type of block is manufactured from cement, sand, and aggregates. They are durable, have high thermal mass and high strength. The blocks are heavy to use (requiring more substantial foundations) and have poor insulating properties. Dense hollow blocks are commonly used below ground level and can be used for constructing small retaining walls, whereby reinforcing bars are cast into a suitable foundation and extend up through the hollow area of the block, which is then filled with concrete.

'Photo showing a dense hollow block retaining wall under construction.'

'Photo showing a typical vertical crack beneath a window opening due to the omission of an external movement joint.'

6.3.1.2 Lightweight block

Lightweight blocks are manufactured from cement, together with a variety of natural or man-made aggregates. Their main advantage over dense concrete blocks comes from higher insulating properties and their lighter weight. The density of the aggregate is generally proportional to the strength of the block.

6.3.1.3 Aerated concrete (aircrete)

Aerated, also known as aircrete blocks are the lightest concrete block and their structural application is usually limited to low rise construction or non-loadbearing partitions.

Art stone (artificial stone) blocks were commonly used as the facing skin of cavity walls. These blocks are made from concrete and exhibit similar properties to concrete blockwork walls See BD 6.3.2.'

6.3.2 What to look out for

Building in blockwork requires the incorporation of movement joints spaced at approximately 6m apart, which is half the recommended distance for clay bricks. If movement joints are not provided, vertical cracks can appear. See BD7

6.4 Mortar

Mortar mix proportions depend upon the type of masonry specified, the

strength requirement and the exposure condition. It is important that the mortar is weaker than the strength of the masonry (brick/block/stone) as if a failure was to occur, it should be within the mortar. The use of a strong hard mortar with weak masonry may result in the surface of the masonry being damaged before the mortar (see photo right). Generally, the mortar mix will increase in strength/hardness as more cement is added.

6.4.1 Pointing

This is the visible finish of the mortar. Its main purpose is to remove water from the brickwork joint and should be chosen to suit the type of

masonry unit. Often the pointing is wrongly chosen for appearance, which can result in water penetrating into the building or a reduction in the strength of the mortar if it is deeply recessed.

The inappropriate use of proud joint pointing (which is usually found in repairs to stone walls) can sometimes be brittle and crack or provide a ledge for standing water which can increase the risk of premature deterioration of the building materials.

'PHOTO ABOVE SHOWING PROUD JOINT POINTING.'

6.4.2 Inconsistency and choice of mix

If the mortar mix is not properly specified, the performance of the wall will be affected. The specification of the mix should be carefully chosen when carrying out repairs or building new walls.

Lime mortars were used in old buildings and can respond to minor movements without cracking and can have the ability to reform if cracks should appear. By using a strong repair mortar in old buildings instead of a lime rich mortar, the masonry units can become damaged and brittle cracks can appear. (See BD6.4)

'The colour of the mortar provides a good indication of the mix. A grey colour and smooth face can suggest a cement rich mix, which has a hard surface and cannot be easily marked. A yellow colour and gritty texture, which can be marked and sometimes removed by finger pressure, suggests a sandy mix. A pale white /yellow colour, which can be marked and sometimes removed by finger pressure, suggests a lime mortar. Laboratory testing can be used to determine the actual mix.'

6.4.3 Chemical attack of mortars

Expansion followed by progressive disintegration can take place in ordinary Portland cement products such as mortar, when they come into contact with soluble sulphates (usually salts dissolved in rain or ground water). These sulphates (salts) can be present in clay bricks. See BD 15

'A photo taken of a chimney breast located within a loft space showing a soft lime mortar which can be easily marked and removed.'

BD7 Walls - Thermal & Moisture Movement

When different building materials are exposed to changes in temperature or moisture, they can expand and/or contract. This can cause distortion or cracking if allowance for this type of movement has not been provided.

7.1 What to look out for

▸ Cracks typically travel in a vertical direction, are generally uniform in width and do not pass through the damp proof course (unless it is particularly high).

▸ Cracks are usually located centrally in large panels of masonry, beneath openings or at corners of buildings and do not usually appear through both skins of a cavity wall.

▸ Clay brickwork can overhang the masonry at damp proof course level and can become pushed out of line, particularly at corners and in parapet walls. This type of movement occurs when new bricks absorb atmospheric moisture and expand, usually occurring soon after construction. It is irreversible and not progressive. See also BD15

▸ The drying out of building materials in new houses can cause quite noticeable cracks to appear. See also BD20.1.3

▸ Shear cracks can appear along the length of a wall beneath an expanding and contracting concrete roof slab, which is sometimes combined with rotation or cracking of the supporting wall.

'The building located at each end of a long terrace of properties can be vulnerable to this type of movement, particularly where there is a lack of movement joints. Sometimes referred to as the bookend effect.'

'When debris collects in a crack it can keep getting wider, which is sometimes referred to as the ratchet effect.'

UP

VERTICAL
MOVEMENT
JOINT

'Photo showing the expansion of the top course of brickwork lifting the pier, as the vertical movement joint has not been made continuous through the wall. Note that old movement joints can become defective and should be checked and renewed if necessary.'

7.2 Why has it happened

Building materials move, expand and contract differently when exposed to temperature or moisture variations. Variations in temperature can be significant on roofs, sunny elevations and in non-insulated parts of the structure, which, when combined with local restraint variations (positions of wall ties and the damp proof course), cracks and distortions can appear. In the initial stages, new clay brickwork can expand, which is usually irreversible, whilst new calcium silicate bricks, new concrete blocks and cement based products, can shrink.

7.3 What to do now

Dependent upon the size of the cracks, it may be necessary to confirm the cause of the damage by monitoring. Once the mechanism and reason for the cracking has been established, panels of masonry can be strengthened using bed joint reinforcement, movement joints and/or horizontal slip joints (such as damp proof courses). In the case of a concrete roof, temperature variations could be reduced by insulating or providing a reflective roof covering.

'AS A GUIDE, VERTICAL MOVEMENT JOINTS IN CLAY BRICKWORK WALLS SHOULD BE CONSTRUCTED IN EVERY 12M OF WALL LENGTH (6M FROM CORNERS), REDUCING TO APPROXIMATELY 6M FOR CALCIUM SILICATE BRICKS AND CONCRETE BLOCKS. THE POSITION OF A VERTICAL MOVEMENT JOINT SHOULD BE CAREFULLY PLANNED TO AVOID OVERLOADING SMALL OR SLENDER WALL PANELS.'

BD8 Walls - Cracks Above Openings

8.1 What to look out for

Cracking which usually appears in a diagonal or triangular pattern and dislodged brickwork above openings in the wall, sometimes causing doors and windows to stick and not open freely.

'Photo right showing lintel failure which can sometimes be caused by the movement of supporting walls or foundations.'

8.2 Why has it happened

◄ Gradual deterioration and decay of timber lintels (which are usually found in older properties) due to rot (see photo left and BD21). Note that steel lintels can deteriorate due to corrosion.

▶ Removal of an original load bearing window frame and replacement with a non-load bearing plastic frame unable to provide support to the structure above. Masonry can be damaged during these replacement works due to poor workmanship or lack of temporary supports, causing the supported masonry to move. See also BD4.2

▶ Overloading of lintels due to structural alterations, such as change of use or conversion of the loft space into habitable accommodation.

▶ Failure of reinforced concrete boot type lintels in cavity walls, which can rotate due to out of balance loads and/or overloading from the outer brickwork skin. See also BD19

▶ General deterioration, failure and movement of an existing masonry arch (usually located in the outer skin) possibly due to foundation movement, bowing walls, age, mortar deterioration, general weathering or damage during window replacement works, weakening the arch form.

8.3 What to do now

In cases where damage is severe or if repairs are inappropriate, it may be necessary to install a new lintel or beam and rebuild the section of masonry wall above.

'Sometimes the outer panel of masonry above the opening can be repaired and strengthened using stainless steel reinforcement bars.'

'When installed they create a deep masonry beam which can span over the opening. Dislodged bricks and mortar joints can be strengthened and tied into place using additional stainless-steel reinforcement bars/ties.'

'Indicative detail showing positions of reinforcement bars and ties (in red) which have been used to repair a failed arch lintel. These ties and bars are usually designed and installed by a specialist repair contractor.'

'Horizontal cracking patterns above internal or external openings, usually in plastered or rendered finishes, which follow the profile of a lintel (usually concrete or timber) can be caused by differential thermal movements between the lintel and the surrounding masonry and brittle plaster (see photo right). Small horizontal cracks around concrete lintels can be repaired with flexible filler and redecorated, although it is possible that they may re-appear or open and close with changes in temperature and moisture.' See BD7

BD9 Walls - Undulating Masonry Walls

9.1 What to look out for

▶ Undulating, cracking, buckling, bowing or localised bulging of masonry walls.

▶ Gaps and cracks between internal floors and/or walls and vertical cracks adjacent to openings.

9.2 Why has it happened

Walls can bulge due to delaminated masonry in solid or cavity walls which have been constructed using two skins. The two skins can become separated due to the lack of ties and/or bond (see BD10), caused by general deterioration or poor construction.

Gradual movement of large or slender unrestrained masonry wall panels can occur when the wall has not been bonded at right angles to other walls or tied to intermediate floors or the roof structure.

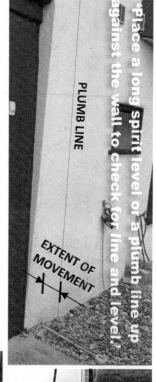

PLUMB LINE

'Place a long spirit level or a plumb line up against the wall to check for line and level.'

EXTENT OF MOVEMENT

'Photo showing new cracks adjacent to a previous repair indicating the progressive movement of a bowing wall.'

'Photo showing a external masonry cavity wall leaning in an outward direction.'

'Note that walls in old buildings are more likely to suffer from a lack of restraint and that walls in any building can be built out of plumb due to poor workmanship.'

The damage can be caused or made worse due to previous structural alterations, such as, overloading walls or from the removal of supporting floors, chimneys and/or buttress walls. See BD24

9.3 What to do now

An external wall could be buttressed, using piers. Built up against the wall or could be tied back to the structure using restraint straps or through the floor joists by installing stainless steel bars. These steel bars can be resin fixed into the outer leaf or secured using buttress plates (installed by specialists), possibly combined with the installation of new wall ties in cavity walls.

'As a rough guide when a wall is out of plumb by 1/3 x the wall thickness, advice should be sought from a Structural Engineer as it is likely that the wall will need to be rebuilt or strengthened.'

See indicative detail below

Buttress plate (if required)

Bowing wall tied back to the floor structure using stainless steel bars through the floor joists

Existing joists

'Photo left showing buttress plates and piers providing restraint to an external masonry wall.'

'If the use of buttress piers or plates are not appropriate, particularly where the damage is severe or where restraint has been completely removed, it may be necessary to locally demolish, rebuild and strengthen the wall in stages, as leaning or bowing walls can suddenly fail.'

BD10 Walls - Wall Tie Failure in Cavity Walls

10.1 What to look out for

Horizontal cracks, splitting or fractures in the mortar joints at approximately 450mm vertical centres and/or a bulging or undulating wall, usually appearing worse in the outer leaf of a masonry wall.

'A rust covered expanded wall tie visible in the mortar joint.'

'The position of wall ties can be found by using a metal detector and the condition of wall ties can be determined by drilling a small hole in the wall and inspecting them using a borescope. This can be difficult if the cavity has been filled with insulation, but possible by removing a small area of the masonry wall.'

'Severe expansion of corroded wall ties in the outer masonry skin of a cavity wall can result in upward vertical movement of the wall, potentially redistributing building loads and forces, (such as lifting and/or providing support to the roof structure) which can overload or overstress building elements and foundations.'

10.2 Why has it happened

When moisture is allowed to penetrate into the cavity or if there are high levels of calcium chloride in the mortar mix (confirmed by laboratory testing) steel ties can corrode, expand and fail (See also BD19.2.2). Other causes include poor workmanship, poor choice of materials and inadequate provision of ties.

10.3 What to do now

In some cases, the defective wall ties will need to be removed or isolated and new wall ties installed (by a specialist contractor) to suit the existing wall construction and degree of damage.

'A routine check may be advisable even if there are no signs of visible damage.'

Photo showing a new remedial dry fixed wall tie'.

'Photos above showing the partial collapse of the outer skin of a masonry cavity gable wall due to inadequate and corroding old steel wall ties. The damage occurred during a period of inclement stormy weather.'

BD11 Walls - Timber Built into & Supporting Walls

11.1 Timber built into masonry walls

11.1.1 What to look out for

The facing skin of masonry in solid walls can bulge outwards, whilst defects in cavity walls are usually confined to the internal walls only. The cracking pattern usually indicates movement in a vertical downwards direction which can include sloping floors and distorted door and/or window openings.

'Photo showing old weak and rotting timber members built into a loadbearing wall, causing the structure above to crack, distort and move in a downward direction.'

11.1.2 Why has it happened

In older properties, timber members were sometimes used as structural load bearing elements in walls, either to support ends of floor joists, brickwork over openings or as load bearing studwork. These timber members are vulnerable to rot, particularly if they are located in unventilated areas susceptible to damp such as, external walls, in a basement or at ground floor level. As the rotten timber looses strength, significant distortions can appear to the structure above, as the vertical support is gradually removed.

11.1.3 What to do now

Rotten timber members should be cut out and removed, in carefully planned stages. Small sections of timber can be removed and replaced with a suitable load bearing element, such as engineering bricks or a concrete lintel, which will stop any further vertical movement from occurring. Cracked or bulging walls may need to be reconstructed, repaired, restrained, or bonded and/or tied together.

11.2 Timber joists supporting load bearing masonry walls

Loadbearing and non-loadbearing masonry walls in older properties can be built onto timber joists. If these joists are loaded for long periods of time, they can deflect and deform (creep), which can cause cracking to walls and the frames around openings to distort.

Usually, the wall will need to be re-supported using a suitably designed steel beam (dependent upon the degree of damage) and particularly if the damage is becoming progressively worse. Sometimes it may be cost effective to reconstruct the wall using timber studwork, particularly if the wall is non-loadbearing.

'PHOTO SHOWING A DISTORTED DOOR FRAME CAUSED BY GRADUAL DEFLECTION (CREEP) OF SUPPORTING TIMBER JOISTS.'

'photo showing a loadbearing masonry wall built onto timber floor members, which were replaced using a steel beam.'

BD12 Retaining & Freestanding Walls

12.1 What to look out for

Cracking, leaning, bulging, brickwork walls pushed out of line/level and deterioration of masonry/render/wall finishes.

12.2 Why has it happened

▶ When weep holes (drainage holes close to ground level) have not been provided, or if they become blocked, water can build up behind the wall exerting excessive pressure and overloading the wall.

▶ Tree growth and/or roots can apply direct pressure onto a wall. Climbing plants can damage the face of a wall.

▶ Foundation movement & subsidence. See BD13

▶ Overloading of the wall due to surcharged ground or material placed against one side of the wall.

▶ Accidental damage.

▶ Excavations undermining foundations, such as ditches, can make foundations unstable.

▶ Where one side of a wall is wet for long periods, sulphates in bricks can chemically react with the mortar, causing it to expand and make the wall lean over the opposite way. See BD15

▶ Frost damage caused by freezing and thawing of water, in porous masonry construction. See also BD6.2.1.3

'Photo showing a retaining wall which has slipped on a damp proof course (DPC). *Flexible materials or slate should not be used as a DPC.*'

▶ Inadequate provision of movement joints can cause vertical cracks to appear.

▶ Damage caused by the corrosion of embedded steel or iron fixings, such as railings and gates.

▶ Poor workmanship, poor design and material choice including walls being built too tall and slender.

In some cases it may be appropriate and cost effective to replace a defective freestanding wall with a timber fence

'Any defect noted should be taken seriously and thoroughly investigated. Immediate action may be required to make the wall or surrounding area safe, as walls can collapse suddenly, with the potential for fatal consequences. Walls should not be altered, or sections removed, without properly assessing the impact and stability of the remaining sections. Insurances may not cover claims if a wall has been neglected. Professional advice from a Structural Engineer should be sought if in any doubt about the extent and/or cause of damage or specification of repairs.'

12.3 Equilibrium

When the action line of the centre of gravity (COG) falls outside the middle third, an object can become potentially unstable and immediate action should be taken to make the object safe (particularly if it is a masonry wall). When the COG falls outside the base, the object will become unstable and collapse.

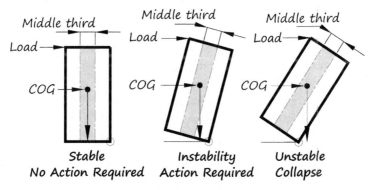

Middle third	Middle third	Middle third
Load	Load	Load
COG	COG	COG
Stable	Instability	Unstable
No Action Required	Action Required	Collapse

BD13 Foundation Movement & Subsidence

13.1 What to look out for

Photo showing cracking caused by foundation subsidence. Downward movement at 45 degrees to the crack...

Pointing to the cause of damage?

▶ Cracks are usually widest at the top, tapering in width and stepping in a diagonal direction.

▶ Cracks are more likely to appear through both skins of a masonry cavity wall, (internally and externally) and at corners.

▶ Cracks usually travel from weak points of the structure such as window and door openings.

▶ Cracks may extend down below the damp proof course.

▶ Gaps may appear around openings (with doors and windows not opening freely - see photo left), below the skirting boards or between the wall and floor junction.

▶ Floors and walls can be noticeably out of level and underground drains and services can become damaged.

▶ Isolated cracks at high level (pulling apart and wider at the top) can indicate ground heave or swelling of clay subsoil beneath foundation level. See BD14

Cracking and foundation movement can be extensive, unpredictable, and uneven. Particularly where the damage is due to foundation subsidence, caused by degradation of organic soils such as peat, topsoil or consolidation of made ground sometimes referred to as landfill. Less common cracks can appear (open and close) due to frost heave, which is caused when ground water expands in the underlying soil, as it changes state from water to ice.

Foundation movements are only usually of concern if the movement is becoming progressively worse or if the building is in a dangerous structural condition. It is important to determine the age of the cracks, as historic movements in properties 100 years old or more are common and provided movements or distortions to the structure have stopped, (which can be confirmed by monitoring See BD13.3.5) and the building is safe, then no further action is usually necessary.

'A photo showing a very old mill building. The superstructure has distorted due to historic foundation movement.'

'The historic movement has subsequently stabilised and the building remains in a safe condition.'

'When concluding the cause of damage, the correct terminology should be used. Insurance policies vary in their definitions & do not usually cover movements caused by the term settlement which describes initial ground movement due to the weight of a new building. This type of movement is not normally progressive or severe and a building claim would normally be dealt with under the terms of a building warranty.

Usually, the insured risk is referred to as subsidence, heave or landslip and if the property is showing signs of any of these defects and is insured, the insurance company should be notified of a possible claim as soon as a defect is discovered and identified.'

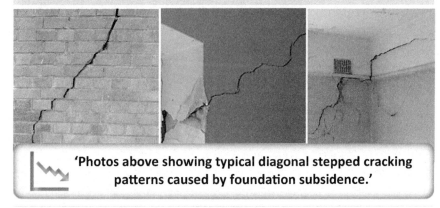

'Photos above showing typical diagonal stepped cracking patterns caused by foundation subsidence.'

13.2 Why has it happened

13.2.1 Clay soils

Firm clays often have the potential to provide support to

> **'THE MINIMUM DEPTH FOR NEW FOUNDATIONS IN COHESIVE SOILS, IS USUALLY DERIVED FROM THE VOLUME CHANGE POTENTIAL OF THE CLAY.'**

the structure above, however clay soils are susceptible to shrinkage, heave (swelling) or softening, as a result of moisture content variations. This can be caused by tree root action (drying soils to over 3m below ground level), a leaking underground service and/or drainage pipe or by seasonal moisture content variations.

13.2.1.1 Desiccation of clay soils – *Soils being dryer than their natural state, causing clay shrinkage* See also BD14

One of the most common causes of desiccation is a reduction in soil moisture by tree root action. In the absence of a high-water table, tree roots will reduce the soil moisture level to maintain growth. During long periods of rainfall (usually taking place over the winter months), some replacement of the moisture content of the soil occurs. However, during drought conditions or when winter rainfall is limited, desiccation can occur.

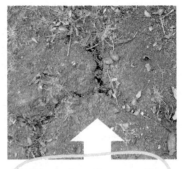

'Ground surface cracks, which usually form in a polygon pattern or shallow depressions around mature trees during dry periods can indicate shrinkable clay sub-soils.'

Desiccation of clay soil close to the surface beneath shallow foundations (up to a depth of approximately 1m below ground level) is a common cause of foundation movement, particularly following hot dry summers which can dry out surface soils.

The effect of the development of desiccation in clay soils usually results in an increase in the strength of soil.

Foundations located within a soil undergoing a reduction in soil moisture can experience structural distress, caused by a loss of support, due to the reduction in the volume (shrinkage) of the clay soil.

Shrinkage of a clay soil can occur horizontally as well as vertically, which can move foundations outwards as well as downwards or sometimes create a gap between the foundation and the clay soil, which can fill with rain or groundwater, soften the clay and reduce the bearing capacity of the soil beneath foundation level. (See BD13.3.4 for laboratory testing of clay soils)

13.2.1.2 **Heave or swelling of clay soils** See BD14

Clay heave or swell can occur in desiccated soils beneath foundations, if the source of desiccation is removed (such as removing a tree). An increase in water content can result in heave/swell as the clay soil rehydrates. For this to happen the soil beneath the foundation level would need to be desiccated at the time of construction (possibly dried out by large trees or if foundation excavations are left open for a long time before construction over a dry period). The extent of clay heave can be theoretically predicted by comparing soil test data, obtained from site investigation boreholes at locations close to and remote from the area of damage. (Refer to BRE digest 412 for further reading)

13.2.2 **Other causes**

▶ Differential foundation settlements and/or movements.

'An example of this would be when foundations for a new extension have been constructed at a greater depth or onto a different foundation type such as piles (to comply with newer building regulations). Movements or cracks can appear or open and close in the wall junctions (particularly noticeable if walls are bonded together), possibly due to unequal foundation pressures bearing onto different soil strengths/types and/or due to clay soils beneath existing foundations (less than 1m deep), which are vulnerable to movements (shrinkage and swelling), due to changes in moisture content from seasonal variations.'

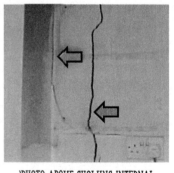

'PHOTO ABOVE SHOWING INTERNAL VERTICAL CRACKING CAUSED BY DIFFERENTIAL FOUNDATION MOVEMENTS BETWEEN AN EXTENSION & THE MAIN BUILDING, BOTH CONSTRUCTED ONTO DIFFERENT FOUNDATION TYPES.'

▶ Washing out of granular material or softening of soils, possibly caused by a leaking underground service pipe, drainage system or a rainwater downpipe discharging directly onto or into the ground, adjacent to the wall of the property.

'SEE PHOTO RIGHT SHOWING FOUNDATION SUBSIDENCE CAUSED BY A COMBINATION OF DIRECT TREE ROOT ACTION AND LEAKING AND BROKEN DRAINAGE PIPES BENEATH SHALLOW FOUNDATIONS IN GRAVEL SOILS.'

▶ Building alterations or changes in use that have increased loads uniformly or concentrated in one area, such as under beam bearings or chimneys.

▶ Sloping ground eroding, becoming unstable or degrading, sometimes combined with inadequate steps in a foundation. Clay soils on a sloping site can slowly move down the slope (creep), particularly if the slope gradient exceeds approximately 1 in 10.

▶ Movement caused by adjacent excavations undermining existing foundations.

'Photo showing undermining of an adjacent property during garden excavations.'

▶ Heave due to frost, which usually affects frost susceptible soil, such as silt, fine sand and chalk beneath shallow foundations in severely exposed areas, areas with a high-water table or after periods of rainfall. Cracks can open and close when water expands and contracts in the soil, as it changes state from water - ice - water.

▶ Consolidation of made ground/fill material or degradation of soil such as peat, topsoil, rotting timber or landfill waste. This type of soil/material is not usually suitable for supporting buildings. In some cases, fill material can heave (swell), particularly if there is a high content of material which can expand.

▶ Landslip of river valleys, cliffs and deep cuttings.

▶ Deep seated ground instability caused by natural/geological faults or sink/swallow holes, which can be formed by underground streams dissolving chalk/limestone (see photo right).

▶ Voids appearing due to collapsed tunnels, shafts or mining subsidence.

▶ Chemical attack on concrete foundations, slabs and foundation masonry. See BD15

'PHOTO ABOVE SHOWING A SINK HOLE. WHICH APPEARED OVERNIGHT IN A REAR GARDEN AREA, TRIGGERED BY A LEAKING DRAINAGE PIPE.'

13.3 Survey and investigation stage

13.3.1 Record crack damage
A full and detailed record of external and internal crack damage should be made by marking up sketches or drawings of the building layout plans and elevations, recording crack widths and the areas of damage.

13.3.2 Record distortion
If foundation movement has occurred, it is very likely that the building will no longer be level. So, assuming that the property has been constructed level in the first instance, either a handheld spirit level or a brick course precise level survey can be used as an tool to identify whether foundation movement has taken place and to determine the extent of any differential movement.

PHOTO SHOWING AN OPTICAL LEVEL USED TO CARRY OUT A BRICK COURSE LEVEL SURVEY

It is recommended that this type of survey should be carried out as soon as possible as it will help with diagnosis and in planning any further investigation work. A precise level survey should be taken around the complete perimeter wall of the building as close to the damp proof course as possible, but ensuring that the same brick course is followed around the building. Levels to be taken at the corners of the building and either side of windows and door openings. The typical spacing of readings along lengths of the wall should be taken at 2 - 3m, which could be reduced in the area of damage. Results should be presented in isometric layout drawing that will clearly identify any distortion.

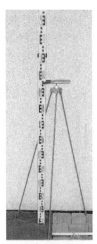

💡 '*If you carry out a level survey by yourself, the traditional heavy measurement staff can be replaced with a wooden or plastic ruler or a piece of metal tape which can be temporary stuck to the wall using sticky tack, which can easily be unstuck and moved from location to location. Alternatively, a tripod can be used to hold the staff in position (see photos above and right).*'

13.3.3 Drainage survey

Underground water main and drainage surveys can be carried out to identify leaks or defects. Particular attention should be given to determine the condition of underground pipes located adjacent to an area of damage. The drainage survey could be a CCTV (camera) inspection carried out by a local drainage company who would provide a report with recommendations. Common drainage defects can be caused by tree root ingress, ground movements and general deterioration with age.

'*Soakaways for surface water drainage disposal should be positioned a minimum of 5m away from the closest point of the building and will not be very effective for use in a predominantly impermeable cohesive clay soil.*'

13.3.4 **Uncover** *(Usually specified by the Engineer and carried out by an experienced Contractor)*

'A trial pit/hole exposing an inadequate foundation and a clay soil.'

Hand dug trial pits/holes can be excavated up against the existing building to inspect the type and condition of the foundation construction and the soil beneath, including checking for the presence of roots.

Excavations should be carried out carefully in a controlled manner to avoid damage to the existing foundation and to a depth that will not be unsafe for the individual digging the hole.

Sometimes it will be necessary to extract soil and root samples for laboratory testing.

Remote trial holes or boreholes can be a useful tool to determine the condition of the foundation or soil away from the area of damage.

The remote trial hole or borehole should be positioned away from any external factors which could be attributed to the damage such as trees and/or underground drainage pipes. The condition of the foundations and underlying soil properties can then be compared for anomalies.

Trial holes/pits adjacent to buildings are usually carried out by hand digging to avoid damaging the structure.

Trial holes/pits located away from the building could be excavated using a mini digger down to approximately 3.0m below ground level and extended to depths of over 6m using specialist borehole equipment.

Usually, deep boreholes will be required if the soils are particularly poor and/or to provide design parameters for a remedial piled or deep foundation.

Photos showing some of the different methods that can be used to investigate the soil conditions.

The choice of investigation equipment is dependent on the depth of investigation required and soil type. Photos have been labelled **1** (for depths up to 3m) to **4** (for depths of over 20m).

Laboratory analysis of a clay soil can be carried out to determine its plasticity and whether the soil is desiccated. As a rough guide the onset of desiccation (to depths of approximately 3m) is thought to occur when the moisture content of the soil is lower than 0.5 x the liquid limit and significantly desiccated if the moisture content of the soil is lower than 0.4 x the liquid limit. This is not considered to be a reliable method for use on all clay soils or on its own and should be combined with as many of the other available techniques as possible including comparison of natural moisture content, shear strength data, soil sample suction, oedometer swelling tests and depth of root activity. Refer to BRE digest 214 for further reading.

13.3.5 **Monitor**

Cracks can be monitored to determine whether they are becoming progressively worse or to determine the rate of any progressive movement. Monitoring on its own will not usually provide enough evidence to establish the exact cause of cracking but can be used as a helpful tool alongside other inspection and investigation techniques.

'Photo showing a vertical repaired crack monitored using plastic tale tales fixed to the wall.'

Cracks can be monitored in several ways. One method is to glue a gauge over the crack (glass or plastic tell tales) or alternatively, for more meaningful results metal discs (demec studs) can be glued either side of the crack and movements measured to 0.10mm using vernier callipers.

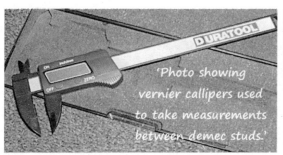

'Photo showing vernier callipers used to take measurements between demec studs.'

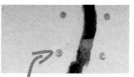

'PHOTO SHOWING CRACK MONITORING DEMEC STUDS FIXED TO THE WALL.'

Monitoring can be a useful tool for deciding whether cracks are related to historic movements or to check the success of remedial works.

'To avoid unnecessary delay and expense, monitoring for long periods of time should be avoided, where it will not influence the outcome of any remedial work.'

Crack monitoring can be combined with precise level monitoring, using an optical level to record the movement of levelling stations fixed to the building (to the nearest 0.10mm). Typically, levelling stations comprise brass screws fixed into a mortar joint, to provide accurate positioning for the measuring staff and located between approximately 1 and 6 courses above the damp proof course level.

Repeated measurement of building levels should be referenced to a fixed datum point, which should be stable. Sometimes, it can be difficult to find a stable reference point (datum) on site, so in these instances a deep datum can be installed comprising a vertical steel rod inserted into the ground (up to a depth of approximately 12m) with a anchored base and with the top of the rod close to ground level, protected with a suitable cover.

It would be common to monitor the building for a twelve-month period over a full seasonal cycle of summer - winter – summer with readings taken every 4-8 weeks.

13.4 **What now**

Expensive repair work may not be required as it is possible that if the cause of damage is removed, such as cutting down/pruning trees to restrict their growth or repairing defective drainage/service pipes, the existing movement could stabilise and the risk of future movement will be minimised. To determine whether the remedial work has been successful and whether the movement has stopped (not becoming progressively worse), the cracks could be monitored. See BD13.3.5

'SEVERE PRUNING OR REMOVAL OF TREES CAN CAUSE ADVERSE EFFECTS BY ALLOWING CLAY SOILS TO HEAVE AND SWELL AS THEY REHYDRATE, SO WORKS SHOULD BE CARRIED OUT IN A CONTROLLED MANNER, SOMETIMES REQUIRING SPECIALIST ARBORICULTURAL ADVICE.'

Should the monitoring exercise show that no further progressive movements are taking place, internal and external repairs can be carried out. Cracks could be strengthened using brick reinforcement and with expanded metal lathing pieces fixed to the wall over the repaired crack for rendered/plastered wall finishes. Where the cause of the foundation movement cannot be stopped, and the movements are becoming progressively worse, it may be necessary to stabilise the foundations. This type of work could comprise traditional mass concrete fill

'Permanent repairs should be postponed until it has been established whether or not the damage is getting progressively worse.'

underpinning, mini piling and ground improvement, possibly combined with strengthening the superstructure using brick reinforcement.

The photos above show traditional underpinning, whereby excavations are hand dug beneath the existing foundations in carefully planned stages, down to a suitable formation level (ground) and backfilled with concrete.

The photograph and drawing below shows a building underpinned using a reinforced concrete raft, supported onto piles. The work is carried out internally and the building is temporarily supported onto props to allow for the installation of the new foundation system.

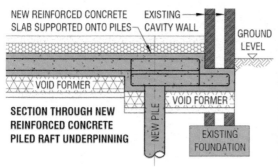 

This type of specialist remedial work should be designed by a qualified, insured, competent Structural Engineer and carried out by a competent contractor (experienced in such repair work) who should provide a guarantee to certify their repair, particularly as this type of work will be costly to carry out and costly to rectify if not carried out correctly.

In extreme cases, the superstructure may be damaged sufficiently that the structural integrity has been impaired and areas may need to be demolished and reconstructed onto new foundations.

BD14 Influence of Trees on Clay Soils

'The intensity of foundation movement caused by ground heave or shrinkage of clay soils is dependent upon; the plasticity of the soil, type of tree, height of tree and distance away from the building.'

14.1 Ground heave (upward and/or lateral movement)

Soil swelling caused by tree removal, can be considerable and movements may continue for many years following removal.

The upward and lateral forces on the foundations can cause cracking and distortion to the building superstructure. When forces act centrally, a crack would usually appear straight rather than diagonal and widest at the top. When forces act on the corner of the building, a crack would usually be wider near the foundation level and narrower at the top.

14.2 Ground shrinkage (downward and/or lateral movement)

Cracks are usually widest at the top, tapering in width and stepping in a diagonal direction.

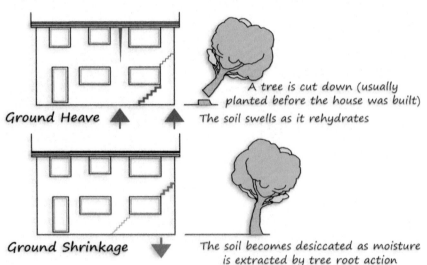

Ground Heave

A tree is cut down (usually planted before the house was built)
The soil swells as it rehydrates

Ground Shrinkage

The soil becomes desiccated as moisture is extracted by tree root action

In both cases (ground heave and shrinkage) cracks usually appear internally and externally from weak points of the structure, such as openings, and may extend down below the damp proof course.

BD15 Chemical Attack

'**Expansion** then **progressive disintegration** can take place in ordinary Portland cement products such as mortar, render and concrete when they come into contact with soluble sulphates (usually salts dissolved in rain or ground water). These sulphates (salts) can be present in clay bricks, the ground and in fill material. The potential risk of sulphate attack increases in materials with a high cement content.'

15.1 What to look out for in Masonry

▶ Horizontal cracking on the inner leaf of a cavity wall usually at roof level (or lower down in solid brickwork walls) due to the expansion of the mortar joints on the exposed brick outer leaf, which can show little signs of damage as upward forces transfer and lift the inner skin.

▶ As mortar joints expand, walls can bow and/or bulge between supports and restraints (such as floors and roofs).

▶ Overhanging of the brickwork above the damp proof course (DPC) (acting as a slip joint) can occur in long sections of walls. Expansion occurs less below DPC, possibly due to the restraint from the foundations. This defect would need to be differentiated from moisture expansion of the bricks (See BD7) by determining when the defect was first noticed. It is thought that moisture expansion occurs soon after construction and is not progressive, whereas sulphate expansion does not usually occur within the first two years after construction and can become progressively worse.

▶ Soft fired bricks can erode because of crystallization of sulphates behind the face, which reduces their strength and waterproof properties. These soft bricks are difficult to repair and cladding could be used to protect the wall. If the masonry is load bearing it should be properly assessed by a Structural Engineer to prevent the sudden collapse of badly deteriorated walls.

▶ Chimney stacks, wall parapets, retaining and freestanding walls can be particularly vulnerable to sulphate attack as they are usually located in exposed areas, which are susceptible to wet conditions for long periods. Horizontal cracking and leaning can occur, which is sometimes combined with a white residue and eroded brickwork faces.

▷ Damaged or poorly designed rendering on brickwork walls can allow moisture to saturate and penetrate the wall for long periods. Mortar joints can expand and cause the render to de-bond from the wall.

▷ Check to see whether crystals have formed behind the render to diagnose sulphate attack.

'Photo above showing cracking to a rendered parapet wall of a ground floor bay window caused by sulphate attack resulting in expansion of the brickwork mortar joints.'

> 'THE PATTERN OF CRACKING ASSOCIATED WITH SULPHATE ATTACK IN RENDER IS USUALLY HORIZONTAL AND VERTICAL AS OPPOSED TO A FINE CRACKING PATTERN, WHICH CAN APPEAR AS A RESULT OF MOISTURE SHRINKAGE.' See BD7

15.2 Why has it happened

For sulphate attack to take place in masonry walls there has to be three ingredients, which are tricalcium aluminate (present in ordinary Portland cement), soluble sulphates and water. These ingredients can vary between construction materials and their location on the building, resulting in varying degrees of damage.

15.3 What to do now

For new construction work: Materials should be specified to suit the required construction type and their location within the structure. Sulphate resisting mortar and render could be specified along with special quality bricks, which contain low levels of soluble sulphates. In addition, undue wetting of the structure should be avoided by providing generous overhangs at eaves level or with the use of large coping stones on wall parapets, freestanding/retaining walls or by providing damp proof courses, flashings and weep holes. Expansion joints in brickwork walls should be incorporated at no more than 12m centres (6m from corners). See BD7

For existing walls: The severity of damage should be assessed. In some cases, it may be necessary to demolish and rebuild areas of damage (incorporating the new construction details previously mentioned) and/or to try and minimise further deterioration by excluding moisture as far as possible, which could involve cladding or protecting the wall. In some cases, such as parapets, it may be sufficient to provide new expansion joints to allow for minor movements.

15.4 What to look out for in Ground Bearing Concrete Floor Slabs

Arching and cracking of concrete slabs (See BD18) and/or perimeter walls bulging by direct pressure of an expanding concrete slab.

15.4.1 Why has it happened

For sulphate attack to take place in ground bearing floor slabs, there has to be three ingredients, which are tricalcium aluminate (present in ordinary Portland cement), soluble sulphates (present in hardcore or fill material used beneath the slab) and moisture.

15.4.2 What to do now

Depending upon the degree of damage and the level of moisture ingress (particularly whether the moisture can be stopped or reduced) it may be necessary to break out the existing slab and replace it, as well as the fill material which should be free of sulphates. In some circumstances it may be possible to replace the ground bearing floor with a new suspended floor.

15.5 What to look out for in Concrete Foundations

The rate of attack and degree of damage, usually depends on the type and quality of the concrete. Low permeable dense concrete, which was well compacted at the time of construction, has a good resistance to sulphate attack and if used can slow down the process of deterioration.

'SOIL AND GROUND WATER SAMPLES CAN BE TAKEN AND TESTED TO DETERMINE THE LEVELS OF SULPHATES PRESENT AND WHETHER SPECIAL PRECAUTIONS SHOULD BE TAKEN, SUCH AS USING SULPHATE RESISTING CEMENTS/MATERIALS OR SPECIAL CONCRETE MIXES.'

BD16 Floors

16.1 Structural stability function of floors

Floors are not only required to support the vertical loads placed onto the floor, they can also be essential in maintaining the structural stability of internal and external walls. Floors can act as a tie/restraint for walls which might not be structurally adequate in themselves if they were free standing structures (See BD24). To ensure adequate wall restraint, floor joists should be built into and bearing onto walls by at least 90mm. If joists are supported onto walls using joist hangers, special restraint type hangers may need to be used.

16.2 Floor construction

It is common for the ground floor construction to be different from the intermediate floors, which are usually constructed using timber joists and boards. Common types of ground floors include suspended timber, suspended beam and block and ground bearing concrete slabs.

'A beam and block suspended floor system, can sometimes be found in newer properties at ground floor level, comprising concrete beams in-filled with concrete blocks spanning between the beams, with a sub floor void and ventilated using air bricks.'

16.3 Suspended timber floors

To determine the type of floor construction and to test its strength, stamp your foot down onto the floor. A hollow sounding floor could indicate that it is suspended timber (with a void beneath the floor) and if found to be bouncy or springy (commonly found in older houses adjacent to the entrance doors) could indicate a defect, possibly caused by lack of strutting, undersized or rotten joists. If possible, remove loose areas of floor covering (carpets, mats etc.) to reveal the floor surface.

Long timber floorboards in older properties can indicate a suspended timber floor. The joists usually span perpendicular to the boards between internal/external walls and intermediate sleeper walls at ground floor level (sleeper walls were usually built onto shallow foundations or directly onto the concrete oversite slab).

Look for loose areas of boarding, which can be removed or lifted (sometimes boards are cut for the installation of services - See BD17) to check the size and condition of the joists.

'As a rough guide to check whether the existing timber joist size is adequate, take the width as 2 inches and the depth as half of the floor span measured in feet but expressed in inches (for example say 10ft span/2 = 5ft expressed as 5 inches) plus an extra 2 inches. Note that undersized joists can prematurely fail if overloaded or if they become rotten, as they do not have any spare load capacity.'

Check external walls for the presence of air bricks just above ground level which could indicate a suspended floor and make sure they are free from obstruction, as they are used to ventilate the sub floor void.

16.4 What to look out for

▶ General deterioration of timber floor members due to age, insect damage or rot. *Note that joists built into solid external walls, joists which protrude into a wall cavity and joists which are located below the external ground level, are particularly susceptible to wet rot.*

▶ Poor design and workmanship, including excessive notching of joists (See BD17) and incorrect installation of joist hangers at bearings.

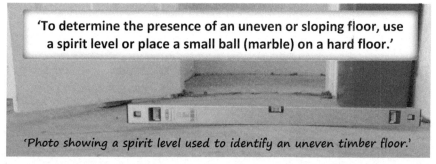

'To determine the presence of an uneven or sloping floor, use a spirit level or place a small ball (marble) on a hard floor.'

'Photo showing a spirit level used to identify an uneven timber floor.'

▶ Differential settlements and movements between sleeper walls (which are used to provide intermediate support to ground floor timber suspended floors) and main building foundations.

▶ Settlements or expansion of fill material beneath ground bearing slabs. See BD18

▶ Overloading of the floor due to change of use or storage of heavy materials.

▶ Removal or failure of load bearing supporting walls, beams and lintels in intermediate floors.

▶ Gaps at the floor/wall and wall/ceiling junctions, indicating signs of movement. See BD9

▶ Subsidence or heave of supporting ground/foundations. See BD13

BD17 Notching & Drilling of Timber Members

Lift the floor covering above timber boarded floors to check for boards which may have been cut for the installation of services. Cut boards can usually be lifted to inspect the floor void to check the condition of the joists and whether the floor structure has been notched or drilled.

Modern building regulation guidance for notching and drilling timber joists and roof rafters is as follows:

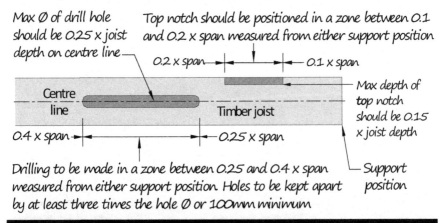

Max Ø of drill hole should be 0.25 x joist depth on centre line

Top notch should be positioned in a zone between 0.1 and 0.2 x span measured from either support position

0.2 x span — 0.1 x span

Centre line   Timber joist

Max depth of top notch should be 0.15 x joist depth

0.4 x span   0.25 x span

Support position

Drilling to be made in a zone between 0.25 and 0.4 x span measured from either support position. Holes to be kept apart by at least three times the hole Ø or 100mm minimum

'Roof connections in systems assembled on site should be cut accurately to fit tightly. The rafter to ceiling joist connection should be a fixed lapped joint and the rafter should be birds mouthed over and skew nailed to the wall plate. Where purlins are vertically orientated a birds mouth joint should be used to fix the rafter.'

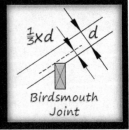

$\frac{1}{3}$ x d   d

Birdsmouth Joint

'If the notching guidelines are not met, if the member forms part of a factory assembled truss or if a notch or drilled hole is needed close to heavy loads, (such as those from partitions, cisterns, cylinders and stair trimming) advice should be sought from a Structural Engineer.'

`'Overstressed joists weakened further by excessive notching and drilling.'`

`'Same joists strengthened using new timbers.'`

BD18 Ground Bearing Floor Slabs

18.1 What to look out for

▶ Uneven or sloping floors. A gap appearing beneath the skirting board at the junction with the wall or beneath doors. Sloping furniture and/or work surfaces.

▶ Dishing, diagonal and/or straight cracks, or ridges in the floor slab. 'Note that smaller fine and irregular cracks may indicate problems with a floor screed (a thin layer of material usually constructed using sand and cement which is used to finish the slab). Wider cracks or an uneven surface can indicate problems with the concrete slab or with the supporting ground or fill material beneath the slab.'

'Try tapping the floor with a metal bar or lump hammer for hollow sounding areas, which could indicate voids beneath the slab.'

18.2 Why has it happened

▶ Supporting fill material or soil beneath a ground bearing floor slab can gradually consolidate due to un-compacted, unsuitable fill material or degradation of natural soil (such as peat).

▶ Sometimes the thickness of the fill material is greater in one area to accommodate level floors on a sloping site, which may increase the risk of settlement, particularly if the fill material has not been well compacted in layers during construction. Note that this type of settlement can also occur on level sites around the edge of the slab, where the fill material continues down to fill the gap between the foundation excavation and the underside of the floor construction.

▶ A leaking underground service or drainage pipe can soften or wash out the supporting soil or fill material beneath a slab, creating voids and gradually removing support to the floor.

▶ Incorrect choice of fill material, which in some cases can expand when in contact with water, causing the slab to heave. See also BD15.4

▶ Ground heave from the swelling of clays. See BD14.1

▶ Poor design, construction and workmanship (see photo right).

18.3 Monitor/Investigate

To determine whether the damage has stopped or is becoming progressively worse, it may be necessary to monitor the floor (in the area or damage) and investigate whether existing drains and services are leaking.

If the movement is becoming worse, it may be necessary to carry out further investigation by excavating a trial hole or core drilling through the slab, to determine the slab construction and condition of the soil/material beneath the slab.

'Photo showing cracking in the floor screed around the perimeter of a ground bearing floor slab, caused by the installation of a shallow hot water heating pipe.'

18.4 **What to do now** if the damage has been caused by settlement of fill material beneath the slab and is becoming progressively worse.

'Photo showing a crack in a ground bearing concrete floor slab caused by settlement of the supporting fill material.'

If the soil/fill material beneath the slab comprises mainly a granular material with no degrading material (such as peat), it can be improved by pressure injecting a non-compressible material through small holes in the slab, by a specialist contractor (see photo right). This material will fill voids, improve the soils bearing capacity and, in some cases, can lift a settled slab back into position.

If the strength of the existing soil/fill material cannot be improved by the technique described above (such as in heavy clay soils or if the damage cannot be attributed to settlement of the fill material), damaged areas of floor would need to be reconstructed using good building practices. In some cases it can be replaced using a suspended floor.

'SOME INSURANCE POLICIES DO NOT COVER SETTLEMENT OF GROUND BEARING FLOOR SLABS, (WHICH CAN BE DEPENDENT ON THE TIME THE DEFECT OCCURS AFTER CONSTRUCTION). SETTLEMENT (ALSO KNOWN AS CONSOLIDATION OR COMPACTION) CAN BE DEFINED AS BEING THE DOWNWARD MOVEMENT OF THE GROUND, OR ANY STRUCTURE ON IT, WHICH IS DUE TO THE LOAD APPLIED BY THE STRUCTURE.'

BD19 Concrete Defects

Concrete is a mixture of graded aggregates, cement, water and air (sometimes reinforced with steel).

To produce the desired strength and quality of concrete, the correct specification, accurate mixing of the components and the control of the humidity and temperature, is essential. If steel reinforcement is required it will need to be held into position during the concrete pour to achieve the correct cover ensuring steel protection, durability and strength.

The performance of site mixed concrete can vary due to workmanship, environmental and building site conditions. The best quality concrete is usually mixed off site in a controlled environment and delivered in a cement mixer (ready mixed concrete). Steel reinforced precast concrete elements such as lintels, beams and retaining walls achieve a high level of quality as they are manufactured under close supervision in a factory and delivered to site when they have achieved their required strength, which usually takes up to 28 days after the concrete has been poured.

19.1 What to look out for

Rust staining, cracked, loose or missing areas of concrete and exposed reinforcement (See photos below for examples of concrete defects caused by steel bar corrosion in reinforced concrete members).

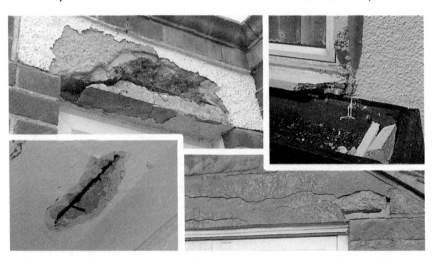

↕ 'When corrosion develops in steel reinforcement bars, the bars can expand to approximately seven times their original diameter, causing the surface of the concrete to crack and break away from the concrete member (referred to as spalling).'

Tips

'Tapping the surface of the concrete with a hammer can help to determine the extent of damage below the surface, as corroded steel reinforcement will sound hollow.

'Impurities in concrete aggregates can sometimes cause a rust-coloured stain to appear on the surface of the concrete, with no visible signs of cracking. This is sometimes mistaken for steel reinforcement corrosion, however unlike steel corrosion this staining will not affect the structural integrity of the concrete member.

An electronic cover meter (see photo right) can be used to determine the quantity, depth and size of the reinforcement bars.'

19.2 Why has it happened

19.2.1 Concrete defects

▶ Deterioration with age and general weathering (design life exceeded).

▶ Poor workmanship and design such as inadequate cover to reinforcement bars, poor compaction, wrong choice of materials or concrete mix.

▶ Chemical attack by corrosive substances present in some soils, ground waters, and in marine and industrial environments, including sulphates. See BD15

▶ The properties of high-alumina cement (HAC) which was used in the early seventies in place of ordinary Portland cement, can change over time, resulting in the concrete becoming porous and loosing some of its strength. This can be made worse if the concrete member is exposed to temperature and humidity.

▸ Inadequate movement joints to cater for shrinkage and thermal expansion.

▸ Concrete can deform if loaded for a long period of time, referred to as creep.

▸ Accidental damage caused by structural overload, impact, abrasion and fire or physical damage caused by frost attack.

▸ Concrete cancer (alkali silica reaction) can occur when silica (naturally occurring in some aggregates or stone) reacts with alkali chemicals present in cement. Cracks start to develop, as a jelly type substance forms around the stones, absorbs water and expands. These cracks can allow moisture to penetrate and corrode steel reinforcement. There is no known cure for this defect, but it can be avoided by careful selection of alternative non-reactive materials.

19.2.2 Steel bar corrosion in reinforced concrete members

▸ Inadequate concrete cover to the steel reinforcement bar can cause premature failure of the steel bar. The correct depth of cover usually depends upon the environmental conditions and the required fire resistance.

▸ Advanced corrosion of steel bars can occur prior to installation, possibly caused by bars being left for long periods outdoors.

▸ **Carbonation** – Action of carbon dioxide in the atmosphere mixing with water and penetrating the concrete changing its properties from an alkali to acid, which corrodes the steel. This can be rapid in permeable concrete as well as in concrete with a low cement content or when the concrete cover to the steel reinforcement bar is inadequate.

▸ **Chloride attack** – Corrosion of the steel bar by external sources like sea water or when built in during construction, if salts such as chlorides (particularly calcium chloride) or if unwashed marine aggregates and/or sands were used in the mix.

▶ Reinforced concrete located in harsh environments (marine/ industrial) or where subjected to severe weather conditions, can result in the premature corrosion of the steel reinforcement bars.

19.3 Investigation stage

Investigation work would usually be specified by a Structural Engineer and carried out on site by a competent contractor.

The Structural Engineer would interpret the results of the investigation and provide a report including conclusions and recommendations. The cost of the investigation should be balanced against the extent of the damage and the cost of replacing or repairing isolated damaged structural members, such as reinforced concrete lintels and window sills. Investigation works could comprise the following:

▶ Site testing can be carried out to determine carbonation in the vicinity of any rusted steel reinforcement. Freshly exposed concrete can be sprayed with an indicator spray (such as phenolphthalein), which turns pink when the concrete is alkaline but remains colourless when the concrete is carbonated and contains acids. (See photo right showing an area of spalling concrete sprayed with phenolphthalein).

▶ Samples of the concrete can be extracted from the area of damage and tested in a laboratory to determine the level of chloride and cement content in the concrete mix.

▶ Core samples can be taken from a large, reinforced concrete member, such as a concrete roof or floor slab. The core will show the density of the concrete and depending upon its condition, it may be possible to crush it in a laboratory to determine its compressive strength.

▶ Testing can be carried out on site, using specialist equipment, to determine the strength of the concrete and a cover meter can be used to determine the quantity, depth and size of the steel reinforcement bars.

19.4 **What to do now**

▶ If the defective concrete member is an isolated reinforced concrete lintel, window sill or similar, it is likely that the most cost effective solution would be to replace it.

▶ If the defective concrete member is a principle structural element such as a beam, suspended reinforced concrete floor or roof slab and the extent of damage is not severe (confirmed by investigation), it may be possible to repair areas of the concrete and corroded reinforcement bars using specialist concrete repair materials and techniques. This is sometimes combined with installing sacrificial metals and providing surface protection (to slow down the process of further deterioration). A concrete repair could avoid the need for costly replacement or strengthening works and could minimise disruption to the building use and finishes.

Photograph below showing a reinforced concrete beam repair

The end of a concrete beam and surrounding masonry wall had been damaged by corrosion and expansion of the steel reinforcement bars, reducing the strength of the beam which required temporary propping.

A specialist concrete repair was assessed as being the best remedial solution.

The loose concrete was removed from the end of the beam and the surface rust removed from the steel reinforcement bars. New steel bars were lapped onto badly corroded bars and then all bars were treated using a specialist coating material. Specialist concrete repair materials were used to repair the beam in stages and a surface coating material was applied to the repair area, with all stages being carried out in accordance with the manufacturer's recommendations.

BD20 Moisture in Buildings

Cracks and defects within the building superstructure (external façade) can allow damp and water to penetrate the structure. Persistent moisture penetration can accelerate the deterioration of building materials (particularly timber), which over time can cause significant damage affecting the structural integrity of the building.

'PHOTOS BELOW SHOWING DAMAGE CAUSED BY TIMBER WET ROT DUE TO MOISTURE PENETRATION.'

CRACKING

'Failure of the timber joist ends, buckling the external wall due to wet rot.'

'Failure of a timber lintel above the window opening, due to wet rot resulting in a downward movement and cracking to the supported masonry structure.'

To remediate defects associated with moisture in buildings, it is essential that the source is correctly diagnosed. This may not be straightforward and can sometimes be attributed to one or more factors. A good way to determine the cause is to continue to monitor the defect over a period of time during different weather conditions.

'USE YOUR SENSE OF SMELL TO IDENTIFY DAMP OR HUMID CONDITIONS AND USE THE BACK OF THE HAND WHEN CHECKING FOR DAMP SURFACES AS IT IS MORE SENSITIVE THAN THE PALM. DAMP METERS CAN BE USED TO TAKE ACCURATE MOISTURE READINGS.'

20.1 Rising damp

Rising damp from ground moisture or other sources (such as a leaking pipe) can be transported up a porous masonry ground floor wall (to a height which can exceed 600mm in wall plaster). Typical causes can be due to bridging an external damp proof course (DPC), such as a raised patio or possibly due to a blocked cavity or a failed or non-existent DPC.

The rising moisture can draw up salts from the soil which can work their way through the wall to the face of the wall plaster, appearing as a white crusty residue.

These salts can attract moisture during periods of humidity and can dry out at other times, causing decorations to discolour, wallpaper to peel and paint finishes to blister.

'RISING DAMP IS PARTICULARLY COMMON WHERE THE WATER TABLE IS HIGH.'

The passage of water should be investigated if internal wall surfaces show persistent dampness (which can appear in an irregular pattern).

Remedial works could involve lowering external paths below the DPC level, clearing out cavities or inserting a new DPC. This type of work is usually carried out by a specialist damp and treatment repair contractor who would provide guarantees for their workmanship.

'Photo showing rising damp which has been left to develop over a long period of time in an unoccupied property. The damp is located adjacent to an internal drainage pipe which was leaking and causing the source of the moisture.'

20.1.2 Condensation

Condensation occurs when moist warm air is cooled to a temperature at which it can no longer hold water (called the dew point temperature). Cold surfaces below the dew point can become moist and wet with condensed water.

A major cause of condensation is from human activities such as cooking, breathing, clothes washing/drying and bath/shower use. Common areas affected include windows, external walls, cold water pipes and toilet cisterns, with the coldest area being affected first. Condensation noticed on these surfaces gives a good indication that moisture levels are high. Persistent condensation usually appears in the form of surface mould and can raise the moisture content in timber to a level where decay can occur. Areas particularly at risk and which may go unnoticed include unventilated flat or pitched roofs (possibly due to blocked roof eaves ventilation).

'Photo below showing the onset of timber decay as paintwork peels, caused by water condensing onto a single glazed sash window.'

The best solution is to reduce the amount of moisture available to condense and provide heating and ventilation to the affected area.

Natural ventilation is considered the most beneficial, however mechanical extractor fans can be used to quickly reduce moisture levels from high-risk areas, such as kitchens and bathrooms.

Heating will help to raise the temperature of surfaces above the dew point temperature.

'Mould will grow in areas where there is a lot of moisture. Large areas of mould growth and areas with high quantities of mould spores can be hazardous to health, causing allergic reactions such as asthma attacks, toxic poisoning, or fungal infections.'

20.1.3 Water entering the building during the construction of new houses

Many building materials used in the construction process contain water, such as the mortar, concrete slabs, screeds and plaster. In addition to this, a great deal of water can be introduced into a building if materials are allowed to get wet from rainfall, during the construction stage.

At the end of the construction process, materials can be slow to dry out, but moisture levels will eventually drop after occupation and return to normal levels (sometimes taking up to a year).

This drying out process can cause shrinkage of building materials, annoying cracks to appear and squeaking/noisy floors. This type of movement does not usually cause serious problems, but it is irreversible.

20.1.4 Flooding risk to properties

Structures and buildings which have been constructed in low lying areas can be vulnerable to flooding. A flood risk assessment should be carried out to determine the level of flood risk for the area from nearby rivers, watercourses, tidal areas and whether the property is susceptible to flooding due to surface water run off during heavy rain or inclement weather. See Section 1-A4

20.1.5 Water penetration

Ground water, pipe leaks, driving rain and snow can penetrate into the fabric of the building through gaps or poor construction details in the structure. Vulnerable areas to water penetration are usually associated with the inadequate provision of a barrier material (damp proof course, damp proof membrane, cavity tray) or a defective building material.

Roof overhangs, canopies, cornices, string courses, other forms of overhangs, including recessed windows, can provide a good barrier to keep water away from the external walls and the building elements.

Drawing showing a typical building elevation, highlighting areas of the structure, which are vulnerable to water penetration:

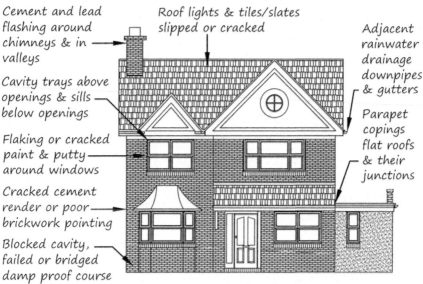

Cement and lead flashing around chimneys & in valleys

Cavity trays above openings & sills below openings

Flaking or cracked paint & putty around windows

Cracked cement render or poor brickwork pointing

Blocked cavity, failed or bridged damp proof course

Roof lights & tiles/slates slipped or cracked

Adjacent rainwater drainage downpipes & gutters

Parapet copings flat roofs & their junctions

Ground water or leaks from underground pipes/services can penetrate through poorly constructed ground bearing floor slabs, particularly if constructed without a damp proof membrane

A leaking overflow pipe resulting in the wall being damp and stained

Ground/surface water and a silty sludge penetrating through a hole in the external wall & into a ground sub-floor void, causing wet rot to a timber suspended floor

Eroded mortar joints, reducing the walls strength and making it vulnerable to water penetration

BD21 **Timber Rot**

'It is essential to differentiate between dry rot and wet rot, particularly as dry rot can be much more troublesome and expensive to eradicate. A moisture content reading of the affected area can be a useful tool to help confirm the diagnosis.'

21.1 **Wet rot (Coniophoraright Puteana)**

Timber decay can be caused by several different types of fungi, which come under the term 'wet rot'. The process begins when fungus spores present in the air, land onto damp timber. These spores require very damp conditions to germinate and flourish, extending yellow - brown thread like strands which darken with age. Attacked timber becomes dark brown in colour and the main cracks extend along the grain of the wood with smaller cracks travelling perpendicular to the main cracks across the grain. Should the damp conditions be removed, the fungi will no longer exist. This type of fungi does not have the ability to spread to dry timber, plaster or brickwork.

'Look out for a damp musty smell and yellow brown thread like strands becoming dark brown with age. The fruiting body of the fungus is rarely seen inside a building. Visible damage appears as main cracks, in line with the grain, with smaller cracks across the grain (see photo above).'

21.2 Dry rot (Serpula Lacrymans)

Spores of the dry rot fungus, can be present in the air and require moist stagnant conditions to grow. When spores germinate and grow, silver grey cotton wool type growth with grey strands, spread over the surface of the timber. These strands can exist and attack dry timber, as any moisture required for their future growth can be taken from the atmosphere. Timber will crack, shrink and loose its strength as cellulose is removed from the timber. The cracks appear in a cube like pattern with the main cracks extending along and across the grain. Eradication of the dry rot fungus can be drastic and costly to achieve. It would normally be necessary to remove and replace the immediate and surrounding area where the building has been affected, which could include the wall plaster finishes as well as the timber members.

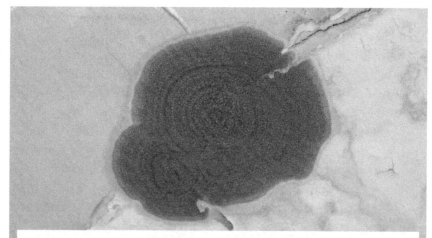

'Look out for an acrid/distinct mushroom smell and silver-grey cotton wool type growth with grey strands. The fruiting body of fungus appears with an orange, brown dusty middle with a white edge (see photo above). Visible damage appears as cube like (cuboidal) cracking with main cracks extending along and across the grain.'

BD22 Modern Timber Framed Housing

'The approach to inspecting a timber frame house for structural building defects is comparable to that used for other forms of construction as there are many similarities, including the overall appearance. Timber framed houses are constructed using a load bearing framework of insulated timber studs covered with a wood sheathing board and finished internally using plasterboard. The external cladding is non-structural and can be masonry (brick, rendered block, stone) or lightweight cladding such as tiles, slates, cement render on lath, timber boarding or shingles.'

22.1 How to identify a timber framed house

▶ Check whether the internal walls have been predominantly constructed using timber stud partitions by tapping the walls to see if they sound hollow (not to be confused with dry lined masonry walls, whereby gaps are left between the plasterboard and wall, making a hollow sound when tapped).

▶ Loosen an internal electrical cover plate on an external wall to identify a timber frame (carried out by a professional to avoid the risk of injury).

▶ Lift a floorboard (on an intermediate floor) next to an external wall to see whether the joists are supported onto a timber frame.

▶ Check in the loft space for timber boarding on gables (end walls) or plasterboard on party walls (if applicable). Not to be confused with localised timber spandrel panels.

▶ Check the position of a window within the external wall, as it would be usual for the window to be located deeper within the opening as the windows are fixed to the internal timber frame. There should also be some allowance for differential movement beneath the windows in masonry clad structures. See BD22.2

▶ Check for many vents and/or weep holes (plastic slots or open vertical mortar joints 'perpends') positioned around the perimeter of the building at the base of the external wall (located at approximately 1.5m centres) and above window openings. The slots are used to allow air flow between fire stops (barriers) and for cavity drainage.

▶ Refer to 'as built' drawings or contact the local authority to view archive records (planning drawings). See also A2

'The photos below show two different build stages of a timber frame. The load bearing timber frame is erected first, then the roof covering and then the external brick cladding, disguising the frame and making it indistinguishable at first glance from a load bearing masonry structure.'

22.2 Some common defects found in timber framed buildings

▸ Timber frame structures are vulnerable to deterioration due to water ingress, causing structural timber elements to rot, deteriorate and become weak. Common causes include poorly fitted doors or windows, the inadequate provision of a barrier material and/or condensation forming due to a high level of insulation and lack of ventilation. See BD20

▸ Defects can appear if inadequate or no allowance for movement has been provided, between a timber frame and masonry cladding, to allow for differential movement caused by initial shrinkage and/or compression of the timber frame and/or slight expansion of the masonry (usually occurring within the first two years of construction). Allowance for this type of movement should be made beneath windows, roof members and in other locations where building elements are fixed to the timber frame and taken through the cladding, such as flues and pipes.

Cracks beneath tilted window sills and/or bowing, cracked walls or, if the rafters are found to rest on the external leaf of the brickwork (rather than on the timber frame), can be indications that this type of movement has taken place.

▸ Insect or fungal attack can be a major cause of failure. Insect attack usually starts at the connections where the end grain can be easily penetrated by wood boring insects. See BD23

▸ Building materials can deform if loaded for long periods of time and this process is often referred to as 'creep', which can result in fractures and distortions in the structure. Timber members such as solid floor joists and beams are particularly susceptible to creep.

▸ Timber wall cladding on gables and wood sheathed internal partitions (racking panels) can provide lateral stability to the structure. The building can become unstable should they be altered, overloaded or become damaged/rotten.

'Structural alterations to timber framed buildings can be difficult to accommodate as the load paths through the building are direct through vertical timber studs. Should these loads bearing timber studs be cut through or removed, the structural integrity of the building may be seriously affected as other building elements become overloaded, causing cracking, distortion and/or possible failure. Similar results can occur if excessive notching or drilling for services is carried out.

If there is a cavity between the timber frame and external cladding, it should be kept dry and well ventilated to keep moisture levels in the timber to a minimum. It should not be filled with cavity wall insulation.

 If you are repairing or carrying out alterations to a timber framed building you are strongly advised to seek professional advice.'

See detail below showing a typical section through a brick clad cavity timber frame at ground floor level.

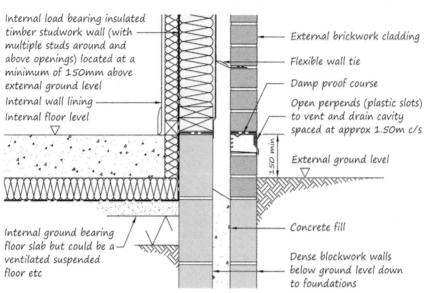

Internal load bearing insulated timber studwork wall (with multiple studs around and above openings) located at a minimum of 150mm above external ground level

Internal wall lining

Internal floor level

Internal ground bearing floor slab but could be a ventilated suspended floor etc

External brickwork cladding

Flexible wall tie

Damp proof course

Open perpends (plastic slots) to vent and drain cavity spaced at approx 1.50m c/s

1.50 min

External ground level

Concrete fill

Dense blockwork walls below ground level down to foundations

BD23 Insect Attack on Timber

23.1 What to look out for

PHOTO BELOW SHOWING HOLES IN A TIMBER PARQUET FLOOR CAUSED BY THE COMMON FURNITURE BEETLE

'Damage caused by wood boring insects can be identified by the holes which appear on the surface of the timber. Newer holes are clean with sharp edges. If the attack is active, bore dust (frass) may be found on the surface of the timber, beetles may be found close to the surface (or nearby) & larvae may be found inside the timber.'

23.2 Why has it happened

Common wood boring insects include the common furniture beetle (woodworm), the death watch beetle, the house longhorn beetle and the lyctus or powder post beetle. The eggs of the common furniture beetle are laid onto the surface of the timber and when the larvae hatch they bore deep into the timber. They can stay tunnelling for up to 3 years, eventually emerging as beetles and leaving circular holes up to 2mm in diameter. More serious damage can be caused by the house longhorn beetle, whereby the larvae can grow up to 25mm long and remain tunnelling for up to 10 years emerging through widely spaced oval holes up to 6mm long. The death watch beetle usually attack timbers which have already been weakened by fungal attack and are usually confined to old large structures and historical buildings.

23.3 What to do now

Attacked timber members may be badly damaged inside and may require replacement as tunnels are formed below the surface by the larvae. It can be difficult to successfully eliminate an infestation and treatment should be commenced as soon as defects are noted. Remedial works are usually carried out by a specialist treatment contractor who would provide guarantees for their workmanship. It will be necessary to get poisonous materials to the larvae deep into the timber or to leave a poisonous barrier, which will kill the beetle when they attempt to bore to the surface, as they will have to do, to complete their life cycle.

BD24 Structural Alterations

Traditionally constructed residential buildings, with walls constructed using load bearing masonry, rely on all the principal building elements to maintain their stability and structural integrity. Masonry walls need to be weighed down and tied to the roof structure and restrained along their length by the floors (usually at mid height in a two-storey property). Internal walls sub-divide the building creating a cellular form of construction, which is inherently stable, as walls are bonded together and buttress each other.

A structure can easily become unstable when significant structural building defects exist or when substantial structural alterations have been carried out, leaving only a few internal load bearing members, such as isolated columns at ground floor level or large panels of unsupported masonry. These elements will be particularly sensitive to movements and could cause significant progressive collapse of the structure if they deteriorate, become damaged or overloaded.

TIMBER STUD WALLS CAN BE LOAD BEARING AND ANY WALL REMOVAL SHOULD BE PROPERLY INVESTIGATED TO DETERMINE ITS FUNCTION BEFORE DEMOLITION TAKES PLACE.'

'Photo left showing an isolated brickwork pier which if severely damaged (possibly by vehicle impact) the building above could disproportionately collapse.'

24.1 Planning a structural alteration

Structural alterations will require local authority approval. Their archive records could be checked to confirm whether existing alterations have been properly designed by a Structural Engineer and checked on site during construction (recorded in a completion certificate issued by an approved inspector).

A property which has been structurally altered or changed in use, without considering the condition and strength of the existing principal load bearing elements (roof, walls, floors, foundations) and/or the impact the alteration will have on the structure, could result in the building becoming unsafe, or requiring costly repairs to make the area safe and then to repair the structure. To avoid this and to ensure that structural alterations are carried out correctly, professional advice should be sought.

> *'The Local Authority Building Regulation department have the power to enforce an emergency repair notice if a structure is in danger of collapse, which may involve immediate action to make the surrounding area and dangerous structure safe.'*

24.2 What to look out for

▶ Unsupported chimney breast removal.

▶ Loft conversions carried out without building regulation approval.

▶ Distortions and/or cracking in the structure above beams or at the beam bearing positions where loads are concentrated.

▶ Change of building use, materials, or installation of renewable energy systems (photovoltaic cells etc.) overloading the structure.

'THE PHOTOS ABOVE SHOW CRACKED/BROKEN TIMBER BEAMS CAUSED BY OVERLOADING, WHICH WERE TEMPORARILY MADE SAFE BY PROPPING AND REQUIRED COMPLETE REPLACEMENT.'

- A flat roof used as a balcony area, which has not been strengthened or constructed with adequate edge protection.
- Use of birthing pools or waterbeds at first floor level, overloading floors.
- Garden improvements such as inadequately designed retaining/ freestanding walls, terraces or lowering of ground levels which can undermine the adjacent property or building foundations.
- Temporary swimming pools overloading underground structures and/or services or surcharging the ground behind retaining walls.

24.3 What to do now

If structural alterations exist and have not been designed and carried out by a competent professional to local authority approval, structural engineering advice should be sought as it may be necessary to open up areas of the structure to inspect existing construction details and possibly make the building safe and strengthen the area.

'PHOTO BELOW SHOWING THE PARTIAL COLLAPSE OF A GROUND FLOOR EXTERNAL CAVITY WALL. THE INNER LEAF OF BRICKWORK SUDDENLY COLLAPSED FOLLOWING THE REMOVAL OF A CHIMNEY BREAST WHICH WAS PROVIDING SUPPORT TO A VERY WEAK WALL.'

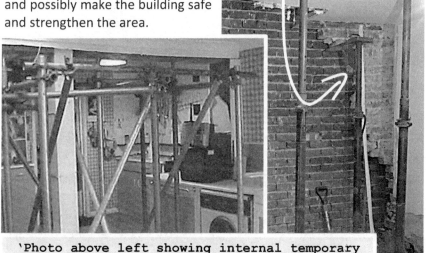

'Photo above left showing internal temporary propping to make the building safe following the installation of an inadequate lintel.'

BD25 **Fire Damage**

A fire can be devastating for the owner and/or occupants and can cause widespread structural damage to the property.

If a structure is in an unsafe condition after a fire, it may be necessary to temporarily support the key structural elements.

Access to the building should be prohibited until professional advice is sought.

Fires can cause cracking, bulging, expansion, distortion and spalling of structural elements.

'Contact your local fire service to request a home fire risk assessment (if available).'

'The loft spaces between terraced and semi-detached properties should be separated with a properly designed fire wall (with no gaps), which would help to prevent fire spread.'

BD26 **Vehicle Impact Damage**

In areas where the risk of vehicle impact is high, such as on piers to garages, walls around car parks and to properties located close to highways, these structures should be strengthened or protected using bollards or barriers.

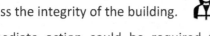

If a property is damaged by a vehicle impact, the building should be vacated, and a Structural Engineer should assess the integrity of the building.

Immediate action could be required to make the building or area safe.

BD27 **Poor Design & Workmanship**

Poor design and workmanship can apply to most structural building defects found and referred to in this book. Some of the more common examples to look out for include the following:

▶ The use of poor-quality materials and techniques.
▶ Chasing out walls and notching structural members for the installation of services.

   'Newer building regulations recommend that horizontal chases in blockwork should not exceed one 6th the thickness of the single leaf and vertical chases one 3rd of the thickness. Hollow blocks should not be chased unless permitted by the manufacturer and power impact tools (that could damage the wall) should be avoided.'

▶ Leaving masonry wall panels unrestrained.
▶ Replacing load bearing window frames with non-load bearing lightweight plastic frames.
▶ Replacing an existing roof covering with a heavier material which can overload the supporting structure.

PHOTOS BELOW SHOWING DEFECTS ATTRIBUTED TO POOR DESIGN & WORKMANSHIP

'DIY roof structure alterations which delayed a house sale until strengthening work had been properly designed and constructed.'

'Inadequate protection/cover to the ends of steel beams built into an external wall. The beams were badly corroded and required expensive remedial work.'

'Cracking and spalling of incorrectly specified hard cement render finish to a natural stone wall, which was constructed using lime mortars.'

'A new central heating system was installed into an old timber frame building, which reduced the moisture content of the timbers, causing large cracks and splits to appear in the timbers.'

Section 3 **Routine Building Maintenance**

'The section which follows, highlights areas of a residential property which should be regularly inspected and maintained to ensure that defects and repairs are identified at an early stage. This will make budgeting for future repair costs easier and help to reduce the risk of a major problem occurring.

The following basic list is not exhaustive and should be extended to other areas of the property where required.'

BM1 Roofs & Chimneys
BM2 Inside the Loft
BM3 Balconies & Parapets
BM4 Lead & Cement Flashings
BM5 Outside Walls
BM6 External timber Windows & Doors
BM7 Basements
BM8 Plumbing Heating & Electrics
BM9 Decorations
BM10 Drainage
BM11 In the Garden
BM12 Health

'Regular inspections, routine maintenance and prompt repair can minimise future repair costs. Neglect can lead to expensive repairs.'

BM1 Roofs & Chimneys

'Inspect the roof regularly, especially after high winds or severe weather.'

Use binoculars to inspect the roof from the ground level and repair any defects as soon as possible. Check that the tiles and slates on pitched roofs are in a good condition and have not slipped or are loose. Check the surface of flat roofs for defects, cracks or tears in the waterproof membrane (avoid damaging flat roofs by walking or standing ladders on them). Check for chimney defects such as a leaning chimney, growing vegetation, cracking or loose chimney pots.

BM2 Inside the Loft

Inspect the loft space for signs of leaks and check the roof structure for broken or split timber members, repair any defects found as soon as possible. Make sure that any water tanks are in good working order (ball valves in particular) and are kept clean and insulated. The loft should be insulated, ensuring that the insulation is not placed tight against the edges of the roof (blocking the natural ventilation), not covering electrical cables or laid beneath water tanks. Look for insect attack in timber members and have affected areas treated as soon as possible after discovery.

BM3 Balconies & Parapets

Make sure that railings, edge protection and coping stones, are securely fixed down to the structure, kept in a good condition and are fit for purpose.

BM4 **Lead & Cement Flashings** (Waterproof Barriers)

Make sure that the lead flashings (the waterproof barrier usually located at a roof/wall junction) are in a good condition and if cement flashings have been used, that they are not cracked or loose. Consider replacing cement flashings with lead flashings as they will require less frequent maintenance.

BM5 **Outside Walls**

Check the mortar joints for erosion, particularly in solid walls, as deteriorated mortar joints can weaken the strength of the wall and lead to damp penetration internally and damage to the wall ties in cavity walls. Re-point sections of the walls where necessary, using a suitable mortar (such as using a lime mortar) and pointing type to match the original construction materials. Inspect the condition of the damp proof course and ensure that it has not been covered over by a raised ground level (soil/paths should be kept to approximately 150mm below the level of internal floors and the DPC). If the property has a suspended timber floor, check the air bricks and keep them clear to allow ventilation of the sub floor void.

If walls are cement rendered, make sure it is not cracked or loose, as water will penetrate cracks and lead to dampness and de-bonding of render (see photo right). Repair damaged areas as soon as possible.

BM6 **External Timber Windows & Doors**

Check that glass panes are secure and that the waterproof seal is in a good condition. Check that doors and windows open freely to allow natural ventilation into the building.

Inspect external timber (including timber window and door frames) for rot and repair any areas affected as soon as possible. Painting will slow down the process of deterioration.

THE BASE OF A ROTTEN DOOR FRAME POST

BM7 **Basements**

Do not raise the external ground levels adjacent to basements and avoid surcharging the ground (storing or stockpiling heavy materials), which could exert additional pressure onto the wall, for which it may not have been designed. Bowing basement walls can indicate a significant structural problem and professional advice from a Structural Engineer should be sought as soon as possible, particularly as basement walls usually provide support to the structure above.

Keep basements heated and well ventilated to avoid excessive moisture.

BM8 **Plumbing Heating & Electrics**

'Check for leaking wet inlet/outlet pipes and connections to avoid timber wet rot and damage to finishes.'

Electrical circuits, cables and fittings can deteriorate with age and they should be periodically checked by certified experts. Do not make any alterations to the electrical wiring without expert advice, to avoid the risk of injury or fire.

Central heating appliances and gas fires should be annually serviced by a qualified professional. Pipes should be lagged in areas where the temperature could fall below freezing and it is a good idea to locate the water stop cocks in case the water needs to be turned off in an emergency.

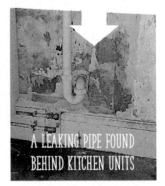

A LEAKING PIPE FOUND BEHIND KITCHEN UNITS

BM9 **Decorations**

Keep decoration and paintwork in good condition as it provides a protective barrier to the building material and will help to slow down the process of deterioration. Pay particular attention to external decoration which will require frequent maintenance.

BM10 **Drainage** Inspect when it is raining or use a hosepipe

Regularly maintain the above ground surface water drainage system by keeping gutters, downpipes and gullies clean and in good working order. Occasionally lift manhole covers to check for blockages and keep them free from obstruction to ensure they can be lifted in an emergency or to allow access for maintenance inspections.

BM11 **In the Garden**

Maintain or restrict the growth of trees adjacent to buildings, as tree roots can damage underground drainage pipes and effect the moisture content of clay soils causing foundation movements/subsidence. Inspect mature trees adjacent to buildings for their condition and to determine whether they are at risk of falling onto structures.

Remove climbing plants and shrubs from walls as they can damage the mortar joints and cause dampness (see photo left).

BM12 **Health**

Identify hazardous materials such as asbestos and lead paints and consult specialist contractors for their safe removal.

Fit smoke and carbon monoxide alarms and test them regularly.

'Always look after your own health and safety whilst carrying out any building work unlike the individuals balancing on a roof top in the photo!'

Section 4 **The Case Files**

Time to put on your detective hat as the following pages contain real life case files.

These files represent a sequence that could be followed to gather sufficient evidence, to substantiate a course of action that will hopefully lead to a defendable verdict.

The cause of damage will not be revealed until the end, so let's see if you can come up with the same conclusion and recommendation before the reveal at the end of each case. If you cannot wait until the end or for future reference, you will find a list of the case studies in the index at the back of the book.

Before taking on the case, it should be noted that structural defects may emerge slightly different in the real world and these examples have been idealised for clarity.

'When you have eliminated the impossible, whatever remains, however improbable, must be the truth'

Sir Arthur Conan Doyle (Sherlock Holmes)

When you find yourself with a tricky case to solve, make sure you allow for plenty of thinking time, which will greatly assist to help solve some of the more challenging cases.

In most circumstances deduction by further investigation will be required, until eventually the mist will clear and the culprit and course of action will emerge.

CF1 The case of the cracking porch structure

CF2 The case of the leaning retaining wall

CF3 The case of the diagonal wall cracks

CF4 The case of the ceiling stain

CF5 The case of the rising conservatory

CF6 The case of the high-level cracks

CF7 The case of the diagonal wall cracks (Part 2)

CF8 The case of the widespread cracking

THE GAME IS ON, LET'S GET STARTED

CF1 THE CASE OF THE CRACKING PORCH STRUCTURE

FILE OPEN

CF1.1 DESK WORK
PROFILING THE POTENTIAL SUSPECTS

Previous section reference numbers A1, A2, B1, B2, ETC... included for further reading.

PROPERTY ADDRESS: Old Farm Lane

WITNESS STATEMENT: *Cracking has been reported to the front porch structure of a detached two storey house. Cracks have appeared around the perimeter of the porch structure.*

A1   Historic aerial photographs indicate that the site was previously used as farmland with farm buildings nearby (now demolished). No existing trees or vegetation on site or existed prior to construction.

A1   The site hazard report indicates that any clay soils on site are likely to pose a significant risk and volume change potential will be anticipated as being high. No other significant hazards noted.

A2   Architects archive layout plans indicate that the superstructure wall construction comprises a loadbearing internal timber frame with brick/timber cladding onto strip foundations to depths of 1m or to suit local ground conditions.

A5   The British Geological Survey website indicates the potential for silty clays and sandy ground conditions. The address suggests that the previous site use was an old farmyard which could indicate contaminated and/or disturbed ground.

A6   No obvious risk of mining or landslip.

A7   An 11 year old building (outside of the 10 year warranty period).

A8   The property is located in a rural location.

TIME TO VISIT THE CRIME SCENE

CF1.2 **THE CRIME SCENE** THE SEARCH FOR CLUES

A9   The inspection took place on a dull and overcast spring day.

A10   The site is generally flat with no retaining walls.

A11   No trees are located close to the area of damage.

A12   The main drainage system is located away from the damage.

A13   No similar constructed properties in the area and no obvious visible external defects to neighbouring properties or to the surrounding ground.

CF1.2.1 **WITNESS INTERROGATION**

Q. When was the damage first noticed?

'Hairline cracks were first noticed soon after construction.'

Q. Have repairs been carried out to the area of damage? 'No.'

Q. Is the damage getting progressively worse?

'Yes, the cracks have been getting bigger.'

Q. Has the property been altered or extended?

'Not in the area of the damage.'

Q. Is the current owner the original purchaser? 'Yes.'

Q. Date of property purchase? 'Eleven years ago.'

CF1.2.2 **INSPECTION** OF THE **BUILDING**

B2   The area of damage is located to the front porch structure which was constructed at the same time as the main building. External cracks have appeared at first floor level above the supporting columns. A vertical separation gap was noted at the first-floor junctions.

Internally, an area of the first-floor surface was uneven (beneath the carpet) at the junction between the main building and the porch projection.

BD5 2.00mm to 5.00mm wide cracks were measured which are likely to have some structural significance and caused by ground movements.

PORCH CRACK DAMAGE AND DISTORTION SURVEY

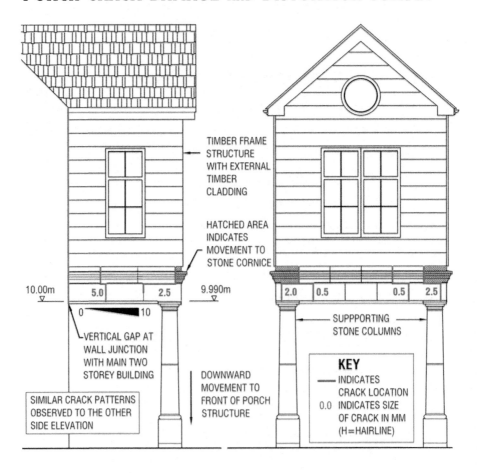

TIMBER FRAME STRUCTURE WITH EXTERNAL TIMBER CLADDING

HATCHED AREA INDICATES MOVEMENT TO STONE CORNICE

10.00m

5.0   2.5

9.990m

2.0   0.5   0.5   2.5

0   10

VERTICAL GAP AT WALL JUNCTION WITH MAIN TWO STOREY BUILDING

SUPPPORTING STONE COLUMNS

SIMILAR CRACK PATTERNS OBSERVED TO THE OTHER SIDE ELEVATION

DOWNWARD MOVEMENT TO FRONT OF PORCH STRUCTURE

KEY
—— INDICATES CRACK LOCATION
0.0 INDICATES SIZE OF CRACK IN MM (H=HAIRLINE)

'PHOTOGRAPHS ABOVE SHOWING CRACKING AND DISPLACEMENT OF
THE PORCH STRUCTURE AT FIRST FLOOR LEVEL.'

CF1.3 DE-BRIEF AT INITIAL SITE VISIT

COMMENTS & PRELIMINARY CONCLUSIONS

A desk study, initial assessment and site survey has been carried out.

The crack pattern of damage suggests that the porch column foundations may have suffered downward foundation movement. Several factors could have attributed to the damage including inadequate foundation design or construction to suit the existing ground conditions. **SEE BD13**

ADDITIONAL SURVEY WORK?

A distortion survey was carried out using a spirit level indicating a downward movement towards the front of the porch structure (approx 10mm). This survey is considered sufficient to determine the direction and extent of movement at this stage. **SEE BD13.3.2**

DRAINAGE TEST OR SURVEY?

The underground drainage system is located away from the area of damage. **SEE BD13.3.3**

INTRUSIVE INVESTIGATION?	Further evidence is required to determine the actual cause of damage.
	It is recommended that hand dug trial pits are carried out to inspect the foundation construction and soils beneath foundations. Soil testing and deep boreholes are not considered necessary at this stage. **SEE BD13.3.4**
CRACK MONITORING?	Not required, as monitoring is unlikely to provide any useful information at this stage. **SEE BD13.3.5**
TREE REPORT OR ROOT ANALYSIS?	No tree influence in the area of the damage. **SEE BD14**

CF1.4 INTRUSIVE INVESTIGATION THE AUTOPSY

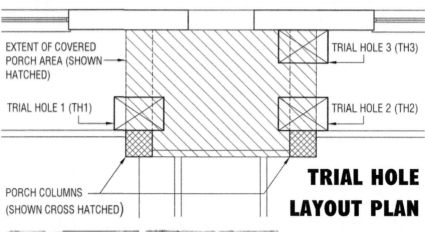

EXTENT OF COVERED PORCH AREA (SHOWN HATCHED)

TRIAL HOLE 3 (TH3)

TRIAL HOLE 1 (TH1)

TRIAL HOLE 2 (TH2)

PORCH COLUMNS (SHOWN CROSS HATCHED)

TRIAL HOLE LAYOUT PLAN

'PHOTOGRAPHS LEFT SHOWING SHALLOW CONCRETE PAD FOUNDATIONS TO THE PORCH COLUMNS WITH MADE (INFILLED) GROUND BENEATH THE FOUNDATION COMPRISING CLAYEY SILT WITH GRAVEL, BRICK RUBBLE (BUILDERS WASTE), OLD BOTTLES AND FINE ROOTS.'

TRIAL HOLE FOUNDATION DETAILS

SECTION BELOW SHOWING MAIN BUILDING FOUNDATION (TRIAL HOLE 3)

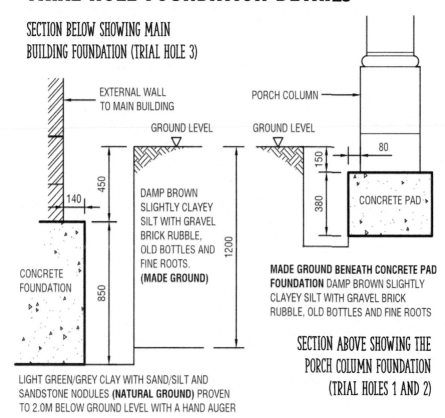

EXTERNAL WALL TO MAIN BUILDING

PORCH COLUMN

GROUND LEVEL

GROUND LEVEL

80

450

140

DAMP BROWN SLIGHTLY CLAYEY SILT WITH GRAVEL BRICK RUBBLE, OLD BOTTLES AND FINE ROOTS. **(MADE GROUND)**

1200

150

380

CONCRETE PAD

CONCRETE FOUNDATION

850

MADE GROUND BENEATH CONCRETE PAD FOUNDATION DAMP BROWN SLIGHTLY CLAYEY SILT WITH GRAVEL BRICK RUBBLE, OLD BOTTLES AND FINE ROOTS

LIGHT GREEN/GREY CLAY WITH SAND/SILT AND SANDSTONE NODULES **(NATURAL GROUND)** PROVEN TO 2.0M BELOW GROUND LEVEL WITH A HAND AUGER

SECTION ABOVE SHOWING THE PORCH COLUMN FOUNDATION (TRIAL HOLES 1 AND 2)

CF1.4.1 FORENSIC ASSESSMENT AT INVESTIGATION STAGE

FOUNDATION TYPE AND DETAILS

Trial holes 1 and 2 revealed concrete pad foundations to the porch columns. The depth to the top of the foundation was 150mm below ground level projecting 80mm away from the face of the column. The concrete thickness was 380mm and the formation level was 530mm below ground level. The concrete pad foundations bear onto made/infilled ground.

Trial hole 3 revealed a concrete strip/trench fill foundation to the main building, The depth to the top of the concrete from ground level was 450mm, projecting 140mm from the face of the building. The concrete thickness was 850mm and the formation level was 1.30m below ground level. The foundations bear onto natural clay soils.

SUBSOIL ANALYSIS

Made ground (damp brown slightly clayey silt with gravel, brick rubble, builders waste, timber, old bottles, and fine roots) was encountered to 1.20m below ground level overlying light green/grey clay with silt/sand and sandstone nodules, proven to 2.10m below ground level by hand auger. Soil laboratory testing was not required.

CF1.5 THE TRIAL DISCUSSION, CONCLUSIONS & RECOMMENDATIONS

Q. Has sufficient investigation work been undertaken to gain enough evidence to determine the cause of damage? 'Yes.'

Q. Is further investigation required to provide further evidence? 'No.'

Q. Is the damage due to ground movement? 'Yes.'

Q. Is there evidence of progressive movement? 'Yes, it is likely that the damage could become progressively worse.'

CF1.5.1 THE VERDICT CONCLUSIONS

A desk study, initial assessment, site survey and intrusive site investigation has been carried out.

The main building foundation has been constructed onto natural ground which is considered suitable to provide adequate support to the main building.

The porch foundation has been constructed at a shallow depth onto made/infilled ground.

The front porch column foundations have subsided (moved in a downward direction) due to the ongoing settlement and degradation of the made/infilled ground beneath foundation level. The made ground contains degradable material and will continue to settle/compress and is not suitable to provide support to building foundations.

CF1.5.2 TIME TO PUT IT RIGHT RECOMMENDATIONS

OPTION 1. DO NOTHING

It is probable that the damage could become progressively worse.

OPTION 2. CARRY OUT COSMETIC REPAIRS FOR AESTHETIC REASONS, NO OTHER ACTION

It is likely that any cosmetic repairs will be damaged in the short term, due to progressive movement.

OPTION 3. RESUPPORT THE PORCH COLUMNS ONTO NEW FOUNDATIONS (RECOMMENDED)

This option comprises the temporary support of the first-floor structure and temporary removal of the existing porch columns (setting aside suitable materials for re-use). Excavation and removal of the existing concrete pad foundations and construction of new pad foundations bearing onto natural soils beneath made ground. The porch columns to be reconstructed on the new pad foundations and all finishes made good where disturbed by the work.

THIS WAY FOR OPTION 3

INDICATIVE REMEDIAL WORKS DETAIL

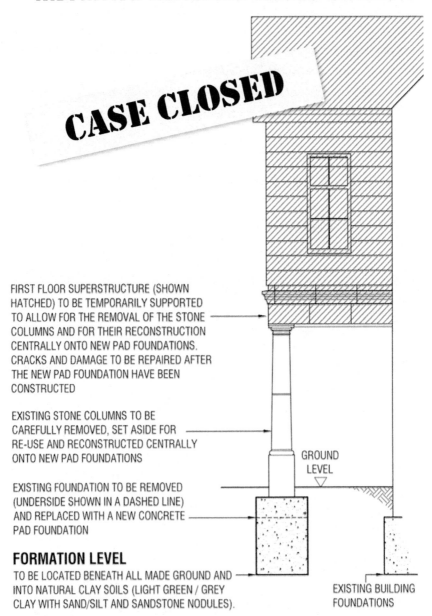

FIRST FLOOR SUPERSTRUCTURE (SHOWN HATCHED) TO BE TEMPORARILY SUPPORTED TO ALLOW FOR THE REMOVAL OF THE STONE COLUMNS AND FOR THEIR RECONSTRUCTION CENTRALLY ONTO NEW PAD FOUNDATIONS. CRACKS AND DAMAGE TO BE REPAIRED AFTER THE NEW PAD FOUNDATION HAVE BEEN CONSTRUCTED

EXISTING STONE COLUMNS TO BE CAREFULLY REMOVED, SET ASIDE FOR RE-USE AND RECONSTRUCTED CENTRALLY ONTO NEW PAD FOUNDATIONS

EXISTING FOUNDATION TO BE REMOVED (UNDERSIDE SHOWN IN A DASHED LINE) AND REPLACED WITH A NEW CONCRETE PAD FOUNDATION

FORMATION LEVEL
TO BE LOCATED BENEATH ALL MADE GROUND AND INTO NATURAL CLAY SOILS (LIGHT GREEN / GREY CLAY WITH SAND/SILT AND SANDSTONE NODULES).

GROUND LEVEL

EXISTING BUILDING FOUNDATIONS

CF2 THE CASE OF THE LEANING RETAINING WALL

CF2.1 DESK WORK
PROFILING THE POTENTIAL SUSPECTS

Previous section reference numbers A1, A2, B1, B2, ETC... included for further reading.

PROPERTY ADDRESS: Hillside Close

WITNESS STATEMENT: *Damage has been reported to a masonry retaining wall which is leaning and cracking. The wall is located in a shared driveway surrounding a parking area on three sides.*

A1   Historic aerial photographs indicate that trees were removed close to the wall and that the wall has been constructed in an area of sloping ground.

A1   The site hazard report indicates that any soils on site are not likely to pose a significant risk. No significant hazards noted.

A2   Archive retaining wall construction details not available.

A5   The British Geological Survey website indicates the ground conditions to comprise gravel, sand, silt and clay overlying chalk. The address suggests a sloping site.

A6   No obvious risk of mining or landslip.

A7   The retaining wall is approximately 8 years old.

A8   The site is located in an urban environment.

TIME TO VISIT THE CRIME SCENE...

CF2.2 THE CRIME SCENE THE SEARCH FOR CLUES

A9   The inspection was carried out on a sunny, dry autumn day.

A10   The retaining wall is in an area of sloping ground.

A11 Trees, shrubs and vegetation are located adjacent to the retaining wall.

A12 No underground drainage pipes are located in the area.

A13 The retaining wall is located around the perimeter of an off-road parking area which is accessible by three properties.

CF2.2.1 WITNESS INTERROGATION

Q. When was the damage first noticed?

'Approximately 6 years ago.'

Q. Have repairs been carried out to the area of damage?

'Yes, a builder has previously carried out crack repairs on several occasions and the cracks keep reappearing.'

'The builders work included the installation of weepholes in an attempt to reduce water pressures onto the rear of the wall.'

Q. Is the damage getting progressively worse?

'Yes, recently the cracks have been getting bigger and the wall has started to lean in an outwards direction.'

CF2.2.2 INSPECTION OF THE RETAINING WALL

B4 The main area of damage is located where the wall is retaining the highest level of ground. In this area, defects were recorded comprising stepped cracking, bulging and leaning in an outward direction, close to the junctions of the return wall. Horizontal cracks were noted to the left side return wall and the damage has re-occurred following previous crack repairs.

BD5 0.5mm to 5mm wide stepped cracks were measured which are likely to have some structural significance and likely to have been caused by ground movements.

CRACK DAMAGE AND DISTORTION SURVEY

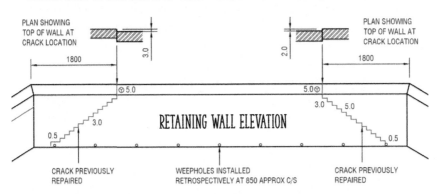

PLAN SHOWING TOP OF WALL AT CRACK LOCATION

PLAN SHOWING TOP OF WALL AT CRACK LOCATION

1800

3.0

2.0

1800

⊗ 5.0

5.0 ⊗

3.0   5.0

RETAINING WALL ELEVATION

3.0

0.5

0.5

CRACK PREVIOUSLY REPAIRED

WEEPHOLES INSTALLED RETROSPECTIVELY AT 850 APPROX C/S

CRACK PREVIOUSLY REPAIRED

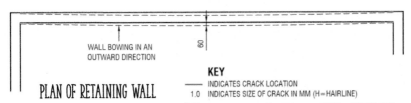

WALL BOWING IN AN OUTWARD DIRECTION

60

PLAN OF RETAINING WALL

KEY

—— INDICATES CRACK LOCATION
1.0 INDICATES SIZE OF CRACK IN MM (H=HAIRLINE)

⊗ INDICATES SURFACE STEP IN MILLIMETERS. ARROW FLIGHT
5.0 INDICATES DEPRESSED SIDE OF CRACK

'PHOTOGRAPHS ABOVE SHOWING CRACKING AND DISPLACEMENT OF THE RETAINING WALL.'

CF2.3 **DE-BRIEF** AT INITIAL SITE VISIT

COMMENTS & PRELIMINARY CONCLUSIONS

An initial assessment and desk study has been carried out. The pattern of the damage comprising cracking, bulging and leaning, indicates that several factors could have attributed to the damage. Including, inadequate foundation and/or wall design, construction and/or tree root influence. SEE BD12 & 13

ADDITIONAL SURVEY WORK?

A distortion survey was carried out using a spirit level and plumb line, which is considered sufficient to record/determine the direction/extent of movement and to assist with the specification of any further investigation work. SEE BD13.3.2

DRAINAGE TEST OR SURVEY?

A drainage system does not appear to be located close to the wall (no manholes, gullies etc). SEE BD13.3.3

INTRUSIVE INVESTIGATION?

Further evidence is required to determine the cause of damage. It is recommended that hand dug trial pits are carried out to inspect the foundation construction and soils beneath. Soil testing and deep boreholes not required at this stage. SEE BD13.3.4

CRACK MONITORING?

Monitoring is not required at this stage as monitoring is unlikely to influence the outcome of the remedial work. SEE BD13.3.5

TREE REPORT OR ROOT ANALYSIS?

Trees are located in the area of damage and further assessment may be required. SEE BD12

CF2.4 **AUTOPSY** RECORD OF INTRUSIVE INVESTIGATION

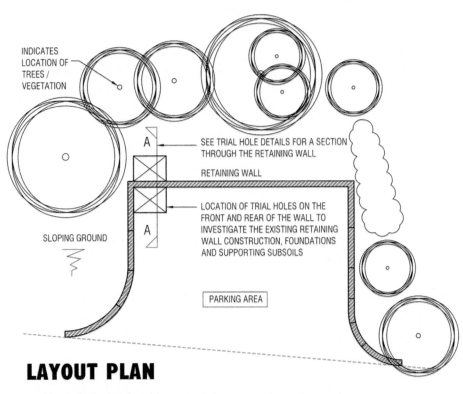

INDICATES LOCATION OF TREES / VEGETATION

SEE TRIAL HOLE DETAILS FOR A SECTION THROUGH THE RETAINING WALL

RETAINING WALL

LOCATION OF TRIAL HOLES ON THE FRONT AND REAR OF THE WALL TO INVESTIGATE THE EXISTING RETAINING WALL CONSTRUCTION, FOUNDATIONS AND SUPPORTING SUBSOILS

SLOPING GROUND

PARKING AREA

A

A

LAYOUT PLAN

'PHOTOGRAPHS LEFT SHOWING A TRIAL HOLE AND SOIL SAMPLES TAKEN BY HAND AUGER FROM BENEATH THE WALL FOUNDATION.'

TRIAL HOLE SECTION A-A
(FOUNDATION/WALL DETAILS)

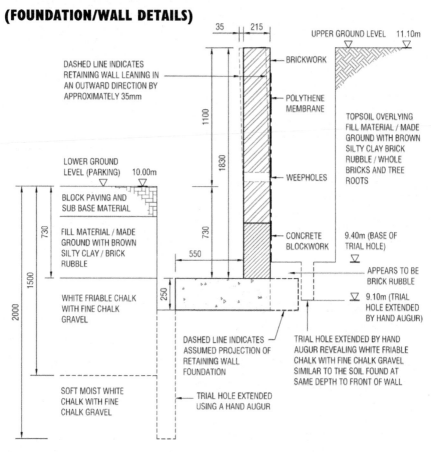

CF2.4.1 FORENSIC ASSESSMENT AT INVESTIGATION STAGE
FOUNDATION TYPE AND DETAILS

The trial hole revealed that the retaining wall was constructed using a 215mm thick brickwork and blockwork wall constructed onto a concrete strip foundation projecting 550mm from the face of the wall. The rear foundation projection was estimated by probing the ground behind the foundation.

The top of the concrete foundation was located 730mm below ground level (BGL) and the concrete thickness was 250mm. The underside of the concrete was located at a depth of 980mm BGL. The overall wall stem height was 1.83m with 1.10m projecting above the ground level.

SUBSOIL ANALYSIS

The soil conditions comprised made ground of varying thickness overlying white friable slightly silty chalk with fine chalk gravel (beneath the foundation to 1.50m below the lower ground level). Made ground and fine tree roots were found behind the wall to a level of approximately 2.0m where similar soils were found as described above. Soil laboratory testing and tree root analysis was not carried out as non-shrinkable chalk soils were encountered.

CF2.5 **THE TRIAL** DISCUSSION

Q. Has sufficient investigation work been undertaken to gain enough evidence to determine the cause of the damage? 'Yes.'

Q. Is further investigation required? 'No.'

Q. Is the damage due to ground movement? 'No.'

Q. Is there evidence of progressive movement? 'Yes, it is likely that the damage could become progressively worse particularly as previously repaired cracks have re-appeared.'

CF2.5.1 **THE VERDICT** CONCLUSIONS

An initial assessment, desk study and intrusive site investigation has been carried out. The pattern of damage comprising cracking, bulging and leaning, indicates that the masonry retaining wall stem has moved in an outward direction as the wall stem is not strong enough to provide support to the retained ground. The wall foundation appears to be stable and has not moved.

CF2.5.2 **TIME TO PUT IT RIGHT** RECOMMENDATONS

OPTION 1. DO NOTHING

It is likely that the damage could become progressively worse as previously repaired cracks have re-appeared.

OPTION 2. CARRY OUT COSMETIC REPAIRS FOR AESTHETIC REASONS (NO OTHER ACTION)

It is likely that any cosmetic repair will be damaged in the short term, due to progressive movement.

OPTION 3. REMOVE THE RETAINING WALL, LOWER THE GROUND LEVEL AND RE-GRADE TO A GENTLE SLOPE

To achieve this option, it is likely that the area needed to re-grade the existing ground, would extend outside of the site boundary into adjacent properties. By lowering the ground level, the existing trees may become unstable as tree roots would be exposed.

OPTION 4. STRENGTHEN THE MASONRY WALL STEM

This option comprises strengthening of the masonry wall stem by constructing buttress piers on new foundations or by construction of a new wall in front of the existing wall on new foundations. The movement of the wall could be stabilised, however the existing materials will remain, including the damage and distortions. Depending on the design of the strengthening scheme, it is likely that the aesthetics of the wall will be altered and the strengthening work may encroach into the parking area.

OPTION 5. STRENGTHEN THE WALL USING MASONRY BED JOINT REINFORCEMENT AND GROUND ANCHORS

This option comprises the specialist design and installation of ground anchors to re-support the masonry wall stem, along with the installation of masonry reinforcement. It is likely that this option will involve extensive ground investigation to determine the design parameters for the ground anchors, which may need to extend over the site boundary. Cracks could be repaired, however the distortions would remain.

OPTION 6. DEMOLISH THE EXISTING RETAINING WALL AND DESIGN AND CONSTRUCT A NEW MASONRY WALL STEM ONTO NEW FOUNDATIONS (RECOMMENDED)

This option comprises demolition of the existing retaining wall and the design and construction of a new retaining wall on new foundations. Although the foundations have not failed, a new foundation is required to allow for the new wall design. An area of block paving would need to be removed and reinstated upon completion with suitable materials set aside for re-use. Temporary works would be required to provide support to the surrounding ground during the construction work.

THIS WAY FOR OPTION 3

INDICATIVE REMEDIAL WORKS DETAIL

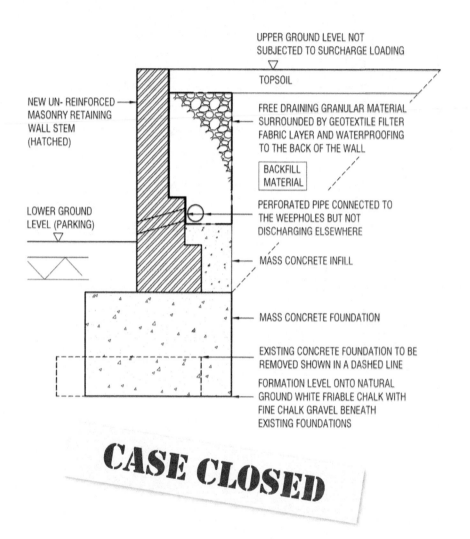

UPPER GROUND LEVEL NOT SUBJECTED TO SURCHARGE LOADING

TOPSOIL

NEW UN- REINFORCED MASONRY RETAINING WALL STEM (HATCHED)

FREE DRAINING GRANULAR MATERIAL SURROUNDED BY GEOTEXTILE FILTER FABRIC LAYER AND WATERPROOFING TO THE BACK OF THE WALL

BACKFILL MATERIAL

LOWER GROUND LEVEL (PARKING)

PERFORATED PIPE CONNECTED TO THE WEEPHOLES BUT NOT DISCHARGING ELSEWHERE

MASS CONCRETE INFILL

MASS CONCRETE FOUNDATION

EXISTING CONCRETE FOUNDATION TO BE REMOVED SHOWN IN A DASHED LINE

FORMATION LEVEL ONTO NATURAL GROUND WHITE FRIABLE CHALK WITH FINE CHALK GRAVEL BENEATH EXISTING FOUNDATIONS

CASE CLOSED

CF3 THE CASE OF THE DIAGONAL WALL CRACKS

FILE OPEN

CF3.1 **DESK WORK**
PROFILING THE POTENTIAL SUSPECTS

Previous section reference numbers A1, A2, B1, B2, ETC... included for further reading.

PROPERTY ADDRESS: Moorgreen Road

WITNESS STATEMENT: *A report has been received of cracking to the front right corner of a detached three bedroom property.*

A1　Historic aerial photographs indicate that the property was built onto an undeveloped site comprising open common land (fields). The timeline indicates that there were no trees on site at the time of construction. Recent photographs show mature trees and vegetation to the front of the property which were planted after the property was built several years ago.

A1　The site hazard report indicates that any clay soils on site are likely to pose a significant risk and volume change potential will be anticipated as being high. No other significant hazards noted.

A2　Archive building layout plans are not available.

A5　The British Geological Survey website indicates the potential for silty clay ground conditions.

A6　No obvious risk of mining or landslip.

A7　Property age circa late 1950's.

A8　The property is located in an urban environment.

TIME TO VISIT THE CRIME SCENE...

CF3.2 **THE CRIME SCENE** THE SEARCH FOR CLUES

A9 The inspection was carried out during a prolonged period of hot dry weather. Ground surface cracking was noted in garden areas, which could indicate shrinkable clay soils.

A10 The property is in an elevated position, on a site which gently slopes down from the back to the front.

A11 An 8m high conifer tree is located approximately 3m away from the front right corner of the building with other trees and vegetation nearby.

A12 The drainage system is located to the rear of the property.

A13 Similarly constructed properties in the area with no obvious visible external defects noted.

CF3.2.1 **WITNESS INTERROGATION**

Q. When was the damage first noticed?

'The damage was first noticed approximately 15 years ago after a prolonged period of dry weather.'

Q. Have repairs been carried out to the area of damage?

'Yes, the cracks have been repaired on many occasions but keep reappearing through the previous repair.'

Q. Is the damage getting progressively worse?

'Yes, the cracks have been getting gradually bigger.'

Q. Has the property been altered or extended?

'Not in the area of the damage.'

Q. Have improvements been carried out to external garden areas? 'Yes, garden landscaping work was carried out, which included the planting of trees and vegetation in the front garden.'

CF3.2.2 INSPECTION OF THE BUILDING

B1   The building construction comprises external masonry cavity wall construction with timber intermediate and suspended ground floors, beneath a hipped roof.

The main area of damage is located to the front right corner and continues along both the front and the side walls.

Tapering diagonal cracks were noted above and below the front single storey bay window and along the side elevation.

The cracks travel down beneath the damp proof course.

The front ground floor bay window frames have distorted and the windows do not open freely.

Internal cracks were noted in the same locations as the external cracks.

BD5   5mm wide cracks were measured which have reappeared through previous repairs. This type of crack is likely to have some structural significance and could be caused by ground movements.

'PHOTOGRAPH LEFT SHOWING THE FRONT ELEVATION AND A LARGE CONIFER TREE WHICH WAS PLANTED AFTER THE PROPERTY WAS CONSTRUCTED.'

'PHOTOGRAPH FAR LEFT SHOWING A CRACK TRAVELLING BENEATH THE BAY WINDOW AND DAMP-PROOF COURSE TO GROUND LEVEL.'

'PHOTOGRAPH LEFT SHOWING A CRACK WHICH HAS RE APPEARED ABOVE THE BAY WINDOW THROUGH A PREVIOUS REPAIR.'

CRACK DAMAGE AND DISTORTION SURVEY

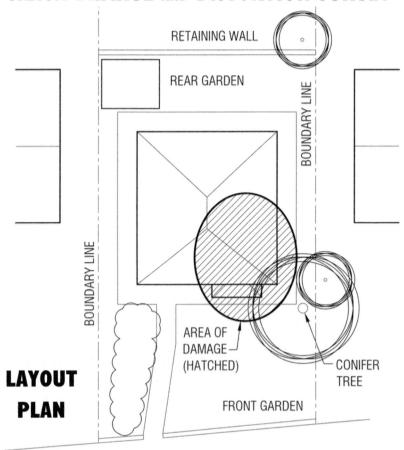

RETAINING WALL

REAR GARDEN

BOUNDARY LINE

BOUNDARY LINE

LAYOUT PLAN

AREA OF DAMAGE (HATCHED)

CONIFER TREE

FRONT GARDEN

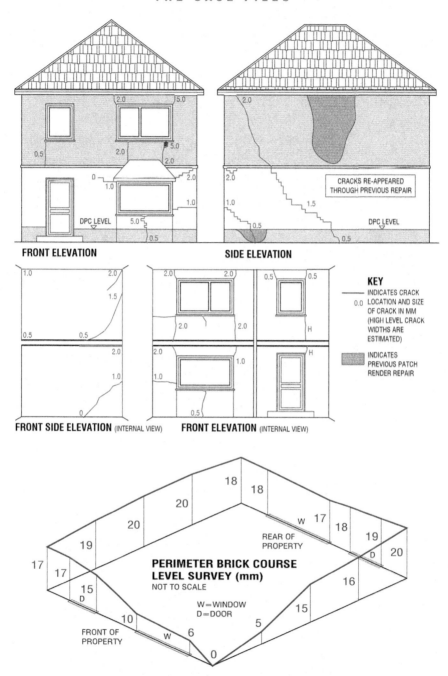

FRONT ELEVATION

SIDE ELEVATION

CRACKS RE-APPEARED THROUGH PREVIOUS REPAIR

KEY

INDICATES CRACK
0.0 LOCATION AND SIZE OF CRACK IN MM (HIGH LEVEL CRACK WIDTHS ARE ESTIMATED)

INDICATES PREVIOUS PATCH RENDER REPAIR

FRONT SIDE ELEVATION (INTERNAL VIEW)

FRONT ELEVATION (INTERNAL VIEW)

PERIMETER BRICK COURSE LEVEL SURVEY (mm)
NOT TO SCALE

W = WINDOW
D = DOOR

REAR OF PROPERTY

FRONT OF PROPERTY

CF3.3 **DE-BRIEF** AT INITIAL SITE VISIT

COMMENTS & PRELIMINARY CONCLUSIONS:

A desk study, initial assessment and site survey has been carried out. The crack pattern of damage and the brick course level survey (which recorded a decrease in level towards the front right corner) indicates that the front right corner of the building may have suffered foundation subsidence (downward movement). **SEE BD13**

IS ADDITIONAL SURVEY WORK REQUIRED?

Both the crack and brick course level survey provide sufficient evidence to determine the direction and extent of movement to the building. **SEE BD13.3.2**

DRAINAGE TEST AND SURVEY?

The main underground drainage system is not located in the area of damage. **SEE BD13.3.3**

INTRUSIVE INVESTIGATION?

Further evidence is required to determine the cause of damage. It is recommended that hand dug trial pits are carried out to inspect the foundation construction/soils beneath the foundation and that a borehole investigation is carried out to obtain soil information, which will be recorded and sent for laboratory analysis (where appropriate). **SEE BD13.3.4**

CRACK MONITORING?

Crack monitoring and precise levelling with the installation of a deep datum is recommended. Initially for a twelve-month period, with readings taken at an eight-week frequency.

The monitoring results will provide additional evidence to verify the extent and progressive nature of any movement. **SEE BD13.3.5**

TREE REPORT OR
ROOT ANALYSIS?

Tree root analysis is likely and will be dependent on findings of the investigation.

SEE BD14

CF3.4 INTRUSIVE INVESTIGATION THE AUTOPSY 💀

TRIAL HOLE & MONITORING LAYOUT PLAN

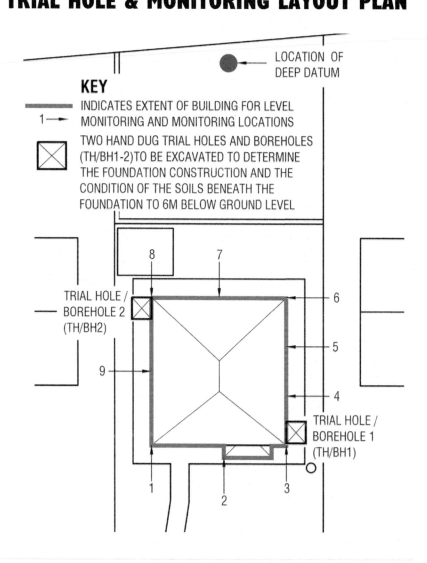

LOCATION OF DEEP DATUM

KEY

INDICATES EXTENT OF BUILDING FOR LEVEL MONITORING AND MONITORING LOCATIONS

TWO HAND DUG TRIAL HOLES AND BOREHOLES (TH/BH1-2) TO BE EXCAVATED TO DETERMINE THE FOUNDATION CONSTRUCTION AND THE CONDITION OF THE SOILS BENEATH THE FOUNDATION TO 6M BELOW GROUND LEVEL

TRIAL HOLE / BOREHOLE 2 (TH/BH2)

TRIAL HOLE / BOREHOLE 1 (TH/BH1)

ELEVATIONS SHOWING EXTERNAL CRACK MONITORING LOCATIONS (A-D)

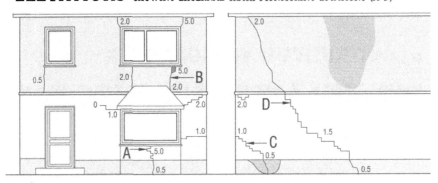

TRIAL HOLE FOUNDATION DETAILS

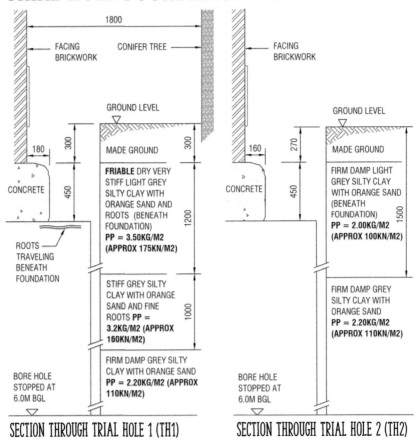

SECTION THROUGH TRIAL HOLE 1 (TH1)   SECTION THROUGH TRIAL HOLE 2 (TH2)

CF3.4.1 **FORENSIC ASSESSMENT** AT INVESTIGATION STAGE

FOUNDATION TYPE AND DETAILS

Two trial holes were excavated. Trial hole 1 (in the area of damage) revealed a concrete foundation projecting 180mm from the external face of the wall. The top of the concrete was located at 300mm below ground level (BGL) and the concrete thickness was 450mm. The underside of the foundation was located at 750mm BGL. Trial hole 2 (remote from the damage) revealed a concrete foundation 160mm from the external face of the wall. The top of the concrete was located at 270mm BGL and the concrete thickness was 450mm.

BOREHOLE INVESTIGATION DETAILS

Two boreholes were carried out. One borehole was in the area of damage and one in the rear garden away from the area of damage (control borehole). The boreholes were taken to 6m BGL.

SUBSOIL DETAILS

The borehole and trial hole in the area of damage revealed: Made ground to 0.30m overlying friable dry very stiff light grey silty clay with orange sand and roots (beneath foundation) to 1.50m BGL, overlying stiff grey silty clay with orange sand and fine roots to 2.5m BGL overlying firm damp grey silty clay with orange sand recorded to 6.0m BGL. The borehole and trial hole away from the area of damage revealed: Made ground to 0.27m overlying firm damp light grey silty clay with orange sand to 1.50m BGL overlying firm damp grey silty clay with orange sand recorded to 6.0m BGL.

PLASTICITY INDEX (SOIL LABORATORY TESTING RESULTS)

A series of Atterberg limits tests were carried out on selected samples which indicated the liquid limit (LL) was measured in the range of LL=73 to 84 and the plasticity index (PI) values in the range of PI=40 to 51, which confirmed the soil to be of very high plasticity. NHBC Standards Chapter 4.2 classifies this clay soil as having as high volume change potential (HVCP).

TREE ROOT ANALYSIS

An 8m high conifer tree is located approximately 3m away from the front right corner of the building with other trees & vegetation nearby. Tree roots were found in the trial holes and root analysis was carried out on a root recovered from beneath foundation in trial hole 1 (in the area of damage). The root was confirmed as being from a conifer tree which is classified as having a high-water demand in accordance with NHBC Standards Chapter 4.2. With the potential to grow to a mature height of between 18-20m.

DESSICATION ASSESSMENT

A soil desiccation assessment was carried out comprising:
- **Soil strength profile plots (as measured by pocket penetrometer).**
- **Soil moisture profile plots.**
- **Moisture content comparison with Atterberg limit test results.**

Assessment of the data indicates that the clay in the area of damage is desiccated to a depth of approx. 2.50m BGL relative to soils away from the area of damage. Heave calculations were carried out using the data obtained from both the control borehole and the borehole in the area of damage using the water content profile method, predicting clay heave movements of up to approx. 25mm (based on the existing soil condition). See BRE Digest 412 for further reading.

MONITORING (RESULTS TO DATE)

The monitoring results indicate that the crack widths are increasing and there is a general trend of downward movement to the front corner of the building.

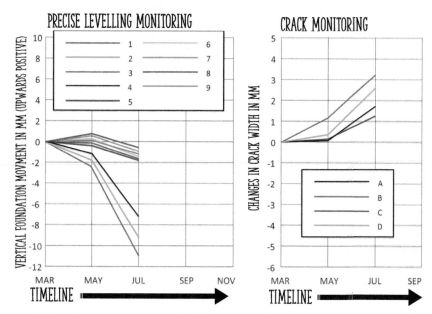

CF3.5 **THE TRIAL** DISCUSSION, CONCLUSIONS & RECOMMENDATIONS

Q. Has sufficient investigation work been undertaken to gain enough evidence to determine the cause of the damage? 'Yes.'

Q. Is further investigation required to provide evidence? 'No.'

Q. Is the damage due to ground movement? 'Yes, foundation subsidence is occurring caused by the effects of clay shrinkage:

• Shrinkable clay soils were found beneath foundations.

• A conifer tree is located 3m away from the building,

• Conifer tree roots were found beneath the foundation,

• The clay soils were found to be high strength, dry and friable close to the area of damage (desiccated).'

Q. Is there evidence of progressive movement? 'Yes, the crack monitoring results indicate ongoing progressive movement in a downward direction. It is likely that the damage is getting worse as the tree located close to the area of damage continues to grow.'

CF3.5.1 **THE VERDICT** CONCLUSIONS

An initial assessment, desk study and intrusive site investigation has been carried out. The level survey, crack pattern of damage and further investigation indicates that the front corner of the building has suffered foundation subsidence (downward ground movement beneath foundations), caused by the effects of clay shrinkage due to root action from the conifer tree, which was planted after the building was constructed.

CF3.5.2 **TIME TO PUT IT RIGHT** RECOMMENDATIONS

OPTION 1. DO NOTHING

This is not recommended as a long-term solution. Movement and damage is expected to get worse if the tree continues to grow.

OPTION 2. SUPERSTRUCTURE REPAIRS, NO FURTHER ACTION

There is a risk of further movement should the tree continue to grow. Superstructure repairs alone are unlikely to be successful.

OPTION 3. VEGETATION MANAGEMENT & REPAIR (RECOMMENDED)

This option would comprise the following:

- Remove the trees and vegetation adjacent to the area of damage to prevent the damage from getting worse.
- Allow soil moisture recovery (clay soils to rehydrate, expand and return to their natural state). Note that it will be difficult to predict soil moisture recovery, which could occur over the course of one season or be slow, sometimes causing lengthy delays before final repairs can be completed. The monitoring exercise should continue and be used to determine the recovery rate.
- Superstructure repairs to be carried out when the soil has sufficiently recovered and the foundation is in a stable condition.

OPTION 4. UNDERPINNING

This option would stabilise the foundation and remove the risks associated with future subsidence. The work would comprise:

- Partial underpinning to the corner of the building in the area of damage to a depth of approximately 2.50m below ground level into natural clay soils without desiccation.
- Trees should be removed to ensure that roots will not affect the soil beneath the underpinning, should the tree continue to grow.
- Carry out superstructure repairs.

RECOMMENDATION (OPTION 3)

It is recommended that Option 3 be considered for the following reasons:

- Tree removal is permitted (no tree preservation order) and the trees are in the ownership of the homeowner.
- The trees are located very close to the building which if allowed to grow, could potentially increase the cost and complexity of underpinning work and building superstructure repair, as clay soils will be affected at a greater depth below ground level.
- The conifer tree is overpowering the building, making access difficult.
- The damage to the building is widespread but not beyond repair.

It should be noted that foundation strengthening work may still be required, depending on the outcome of the tree removal and in particular the rate of ground recovery, which is difficult to predict and could take a substantial length of time (to be confirmed by monitoring).

THIS WAY FOR OPTION 3

CF3.5.3 VEGETATION REMOVAL

'PHOTOGRAPHS LEFT SHOWING THE REMOVAL OF THE VEGETATION AND TREE, LOCATED TO THE FRONT RIGHT CORNER IN THE AREA OF DAMAGE (MID-SUMMER, IN JULY, SEE MONITORING RESULTS).'

CF3.5.4 PRECISE LEVELLING RESULTS

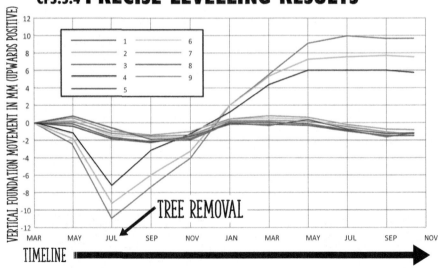

CF3.5.5 CRACK MONITORING RESULTS

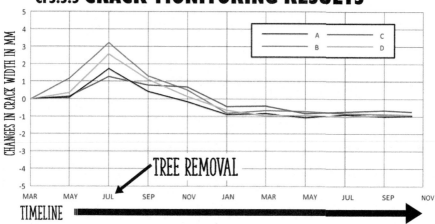

SUMMARY OF MONITORING RESULTS

Trees and vegetation were removed in mid-summer (July). Since removal the monitoring results indicate that ground has started to recover, as the clay rehydrates and returns to its natural state of equilibrium. An upward trend of movement was recorded in the level survey results, with crack widths reducing. The movements recorded, indicate that the foundation has stabilised over an twelve month monitoring period, since tree removal. The extent of the recovery is similar to the clay heave prediction calculation of 25mm and repairs can now be carried out. Future movements should not be structurally significant.

CF3.5.6 SUPERSTRUCTURE REPAIRS

As movements have stabilised, the superstructure repair scheme can be carried out with confidence. Minor seasonal variations were recorded in the monitoring results (due to shallow foundations constructed onto shrinkable clay soils), so it is recommended that the cracks should be strengthened using brick reinforcement.

THIS WAY FOR AN INDICATIVE SUPERSTRUCTURE REPAIR SCHEME

EXTERNAL FRONT ELEVATION EXTERNAL SIDE ELEVATION

KEY

——— INDICATES LOCATION OF CRACKS TO BE REPAIRED

– – – INDICATES LOCATION OF BRICK REINFORCEMENT (SHOWN INDICATIVELY)

INTERNAL SIDE ELEVATION INTERNAL FRONT ELEVATION

CASE CLOSED

CF4 THE CASE OF THE CEILING STAIN

CF4.1 **DESK WORK**

PROFILING THE POTENTIAL SUSPECTS

PROPERTY ADDRESS: Seaview Road

Previous section reference numbers A1, A2, B1, B2, ETC... included for further reading.

WITNESS STATEMENT: Water staining and damp penetration has been reported to the bedroom ceiling, inside a three-storey end of terrace property. A balcony structure is located to the front of the property above the reported area of damage.

A1   Historic aerial photographs indicate that the site is in a previously developed area comprising sea front shops and an amusement arcade, which have since been demolished to make way for a housing development.

A1   The site hazard report indicates that any clay soils on site are not likely to pose a significant risk. No other significant hazards noted.

A2   The building structure comprises a timber loadbearing frame, externally clad using a combination of facing brickwork or render panels onto concrete blockwork walls, with engineered floor joists beneath a timber flat roof.

A5   The British Geological Survey website indicates the potential for gravel and sandy ground conditions.

A6   No obvious risk of mining or landslip.

A7   The property was constructed approximately 14 years ago.

A8   The property is located in an exposed seafront location.

TIME TO VISIT THE CRIME SCENE...

CF4.2 THE CRIME SCENE THE SEARCH FOR CLUES

A9   The inspection was carried out in winter after a prolonged period of inclement weather.

A10   The property is in an elevated position on a site which gently slopes down from the back to the front.

A11   There are no significant trees or drainage in the vicinity of the building.

A12   The main underground drainage system is located to the front of the property.

A13   There are similar constructed properties in the area with no obvious visible external defects noted.

CF4.2.1 WITNESS INTERROGATION

Q. When was the damage first noticed?

'Damp patches keep appearing on the ceiling within the first-floor bedroom, which has been happening over a period of several years.'

Q. Have repairs been carried out to the area of damage?

'Yes, previous repairs were carried out on several occasions to the waterproof roof covering on the second-floor balcony roof terrace (located above the first floor bedroom). Internal re-decoration was carried out at the same time.'

Q. Is the damage getting progressively worse?

'Yes, the damage to the ceiling appears to be getting progressively worse, particularly during periods of inclement weather.'

Q. Has the property been altered or extended?

'Not in the area of the damage.'

CF4.2.2 INSPECTION OF THE BUILDING

B1 The area of damage is located to the second-floor balcony roof terrace (located above the first-floor bedroom).

Water damage and staining was noted to the internal walls and externally around the door opening, which leads out onto the second-floor roof terrace.

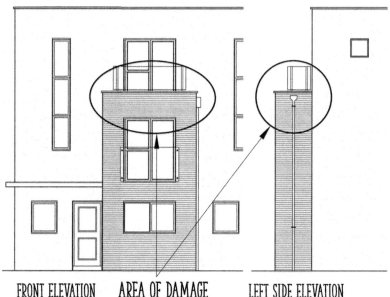

FRONT ELEVATION AREA OF DAMAGE LEFT SIDE ELEVATION

'PHOTOGRAPH LEFT, SHOWING WATER STAINING AROUND THE DOOR OPENING TO THE SECOND FLOOR ROOF TERRACE.'

CF4.3 **DE-BRIEF** AT INITIAL SITE VISIT

COMMENTS & PRELIMINARY CONCLUSIONS	An initial assessment and desk study has been carried out. The water staining to the internal and external finishes indicates that rainwater may be penetrating the structure through the second-floor roof terrace. **SEE BD20**
IS ADDITIONAL SURVEY WORK REQUIRED?	A visual inspection of the area of damage has been carried out. This visual inspection is considered sufficient at this stage. **SEE BD13.3**
INTRUSIVE INVESTIGATION?	Yes, further investigation is required to determine the cause and extent of the damage.

The further investigation work (at this stage) to comprise removing the internal and external finishes, to inspect the as-built construction details and supporting structure. **SEE BD13.3.4**

CF4.4 **INTRUSIVE INVESTIGATION** THE AUTOPSY

'PHOTOGRAPHS LEFT SHOWING WET ROT TO THE TIMBER STRUCTURE DUE TO MOISTURE PENETRATION OVER A PERIOD OF MANY YEARS.'

'PHOTOGRAPH LEFT SHOWING MULTIPLE WATERPROOF LAYERS WHICH WERE INSTALLED AS PART OF THE PREVIOUS UNSUCCESSFUL REPAIRS.'

BUILDING ELEVATIONS BELOW SHOWING THE EXTENT OF THE DAMAGE

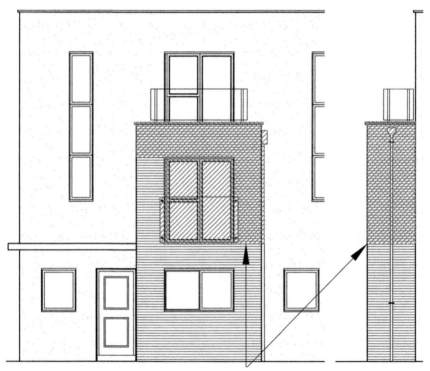

FRONT ELEVATION   EXTENT OF DAMAGE (SHOWN HATCHED)   LEFT SIDE ELEVATION

CF4.4.1 **FORENSIC ASSESSMENT** AT INVESTIGATION STAGE

SUPERSTRUCTURE INVESTIGATION

The waterproof finishes to the roof terrace were removed exposing the timber structure, which was suffering with wet rot.

The damage is significant and has extended down the structure to the first and second floors of the projecting front roof terrace. Water damage was noted to the internal finishes in this area.

CF4.5 **THE TRIAL** DISCUSSION, CONCLUSIONS & RECOMMENDATIONS

Q. Has sufficient investigation work been undertaken to gain enough evidence to determine the cause of the damage?
'Yes.'

Q. Is further investigation required to provide further evidence? 'No.'

Q. Is the damage due to ground movement? 'No.'

Q. Is there evidence of progressive damage? 'Yes, the damage will become progressively worse if repairs are not carried out by a competent contractor.'

CF4.5.1 **THE VERDICT** CONCLUSIONS

An initial assessment, desk study and intrusive site investigation has been carried out. The damage has been caused by water penetration through the waterproof finishes on the second-floor front roof terrace. The previous repair work was inadequate, and the issue had been neglected over a period of many years, which exacerbated the damage, resulting in an expensive widespread repair.   SEE SECTION 3

CF4.5.2 TIME TO PUT IT RIGHT REMEDIAL WORK OPTIONS

OPTION 1. DO NOTHING

This option is not considered viable as the building finishes have been removed and will need to be reinstated.

OPTION 2. CARRY OUT COSMETIC REPAIRS FOR AESTHETIC REASONS, NO OTHER ACTION

It is likely that should any moisture be allowed to remain within the structure, the existing timber members will continue to deteriorate and the structural integrity of the building will be affected.

OPTION 3. CARRY OUT REPLACEMENT OF THE ROTTEN LOADBEARING TIMBER FRAME MEMBERS AND REINSTATE THE FINISHES (RECOMMENDED)

Removal of the second-floor roof terrace (including floor joists/balustrade system) and removal of the first-floor door frame, including partial demolition of the outer skin of brickwork down to first floor level, to facilitate replacement of the rotten timber members (including the timber sheathing located within the wall cavity).

Depending on the extent of the moisture penetration, there may be a period of drying out.

Once structural works have been completed the building finishes can be reinstated including items set aside for re-use (balustrade system /door frame).

The render finishes to the external wall to be repaired to allow for the installation of the new waterproof finishes.

CASE CLOSED

CF5 THE CASE OF THE RISING CONSERVATORY

FILE OPEN

CF5.1 DESK WORK
PROFILING THE POTENTIAL SUSPECTS

Previous section reference numbers A1, A2, B1, B2, ETC... included for further reading.

PROPERTY ADDRESS: Forest Road

WITNESS STATEMENT: Damage has been reported to the rear conservatory structure.

A1   Historic aerial photos indicate that the property was built onto an undeveloped garden site. The timeline indicates that trees have been removed from within the building footprint (see below).

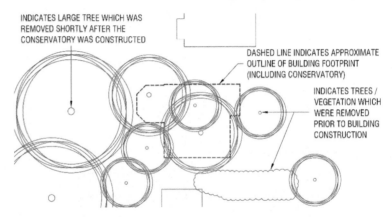

INDICATES LARGE TREE WHICH WAS REMOVED SHORTLY AFTER THE CONSERVATORY WAS CONSTRUCTED

DASHED LINE INDICATES APPROXIMATE OUTLINE OF BUILDING FOOTPRINT (INCLUDING CONSERVATORY)

INDICATES TREES / VEGETATION WHICH WERE REMOVED PRIOR TO BUILDING CONSTRUCTION

A1   The site hazard report indicates that any clay soils on site are likely to pose a significant risk and the volume change potential is anticipated as being high.

A2   Archive layout plans indicate the main building was constructed using masonry cavity walls (rendered externally) with timber intermediate floors beneath a timber trussed roof (attic trusses). The foundation comprises piles/ground beams with suspended beam and block ground floors. Clay heave precautions are shown to the ground beams with a 300mm sub-floor void. A conservatory structure was not shown on the archive drawings.

A5 The British Geological Survey website indicates the potential for silty clay ground conditions.

A6 There is no obvious risk of mining or landslip.

A7 The property was constructed 20 years ago.

A8 The property is in a rural location. The address suggests that the site was, or is, in a woodland area.

CF5.2 THE CRIME SCENE THE SEARCH FOR CLUES

A9 The inspection was carried out on a wet/windy day in winter.

A10 The site slopes down from the front to the rear.

A11 Trees and vegetation (including an oak tree) are located in the garden along the rear boundary line.

A12 The drainage system is located around the perimeter of the main building.

A13 No similarly constructed properties in the area. The property adjacent to this one was constructed circa late 1800's.

CF5.2.1 WITNESS INTERROGATION

Q. When was the conservatory constructed?

'The conservatory was built approximately two years ago, after the building was constructed by a local window glazing company.'

'The conservatory did not require building regulation or planning approval. No layout plans/details of the conservatory are available.'

Q. When was the damage first noticed?

'The damage to the conservatory was first noticed soon after construction, over the autumn and winter months.'

Q. Have repairs been carried out to the area of damage?

'Yes, the cracks have been repaired but have reappeared through the repair and are now becoming progressively worse.'

Q. Have improvements been carried out to external garden areas? 'Yes, recent garden landscaping work was carried out as part of the conservatory construction, which included the planting of small shrubs, paths and steps in the rear garden. At the same time, a large oak tree was removed from the rear garden which was located close to the rear wall of the building.'

CF5.2.2 INSPECTION OF THE BUILDING

B2 The area of damage is confined to the conservatory extension structure. The conservatory was constructed onto the existing building by the homeowner, soon after the main building was constructed.

Vertical cracks were noted at the junction between the conservatory wall/window frame and the main building.

The cracks travel down beneath the damp proof course.

High level cracks were visible at the roof junction.

The window frames have distorted and the windows do not open freely.

Internal cracks were noted in the same locations as the external cracks.

BD5 3mm wide cracks were measured, which have reappeared through previous repairs. This type of crack is likely to have some structural significance and may be caused by ground movements.

SITE LAYOUT PLAN (SHOWING AREA OF DAMAGE)

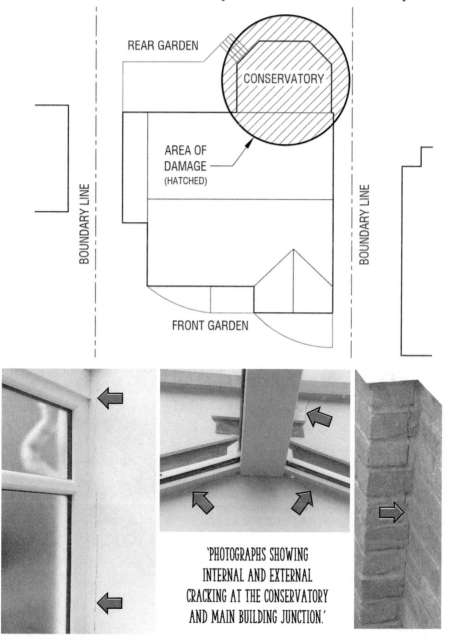

'PHOTOGRAPHS SHOWING
INTERNAL AND EXTERNAL
CRACKING AT THE CONSERVATORY
AND MAIN BUILDING JUNCTION.'

CRACK DAMAGE SURVEY

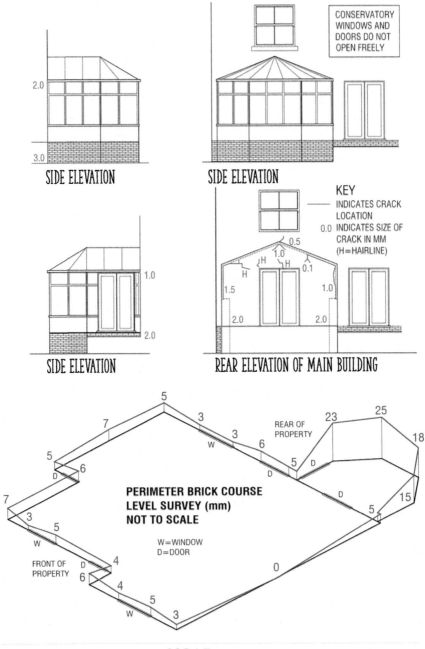

CONSERVATORY WINDOWS AND DOORS DO NOT OPEN FREELY

SIDE ELEVATION

SIDE ELEVATION

KEY

— INDICATES CRACK LOCATION

0.0 INDICATES SIZE OF CRACK IN MM (H=HAIRLINE)

SIDE ELEVATION

REAR ELEVATION OF MAIN BUILDING

PERIMETER BRICK COURSE LEVEL SURVEY (mm) NOT TO SCALE

W=WINDOW
D=DOOR

REAR OF PROPERTY

FRONT OF PROPERTY

CF5.3 **DE-BRIEF** AT INITIAL SITE VISIT

COMMENTS & PRELIMINARY CONCLUSIONS

An initial assessment, site survey and desk study has been carried out. The brick course level survey and the crack pattern of damage suggests the conservatory may have suffered (upward) foundation movement. Several factors could be attributed to the damage, including inadequate foundation design to cater for the effects of ground heave, caused by the removal of trees in clay soils, shortly after construction. **SEE BD13.2.1.2**

IS ADDITIONAL SURVEY WORK REQUIRED?

The crack and brick course level surveys are sufficient to determine the direction/extent of movement (at this stage) and will be used to assist with the specification of further investigation work. **SEE BD13.3.2**

DRAINAGE TEST AND SURVEY?

Possibly, depending on the findings of the site investigation. **SEE BD13.3.3**

INTRUSIVE INVESTIGATION?

It is recommended that hand dug trial pits are carried out to inspect the foundation construction/ soils beneath the foundation and a borehole investigation be carried out to obtain soil information in the area of damage and away from the area of damage (control borehole). **SEE BD13.3.4**

CRACK MONITORING?

Yes, crack monitoring and a level survey along with the installation of a deep datum. Monitoring to take place over a 12-month period (readings taken every 8 weeks). The results will verify the extent and progressive nature of any movement. **SEE BD13.3.5**

TREE REPORT OR ROOT ANALYSIS?	Possibly required depending on the findings of the site investigation.	SEE BD14

CF5.4 INTRUSIVE INVESTIGATION THE AUTOPSY 💀

MONITORING & TRIAL HOLE LAYOUT PLAN

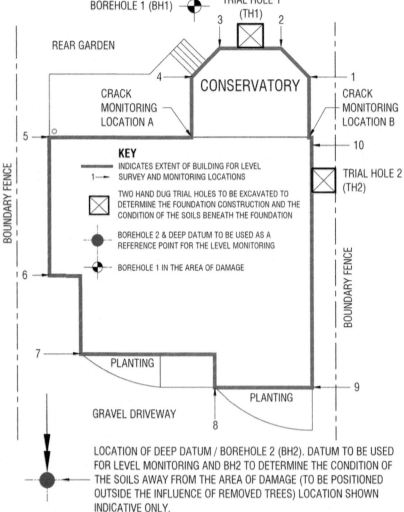

LOCATION OF DEEP DATUM / BOREHOLE 2 (BH2). DATUM TO BE USED FOR LEVEL MONITORING AND BH2 TO DETERMINE THE CONDITION OF THE SOILS AWAY FROM THE AREA OF DAMAGE (TO BE POSITIONED OUTSIDE THE INFLUENCE OF REMOVED TREES) LOCATION SHOWN INDICATIVE ONLY.

SECTION THROUGH TRIAL HOLE 1 CONSERVATORY FOUNDATIONS

SECTION THROUGH TRIAL HOLE 2 MAIN BUILDING FOUNDATIONS

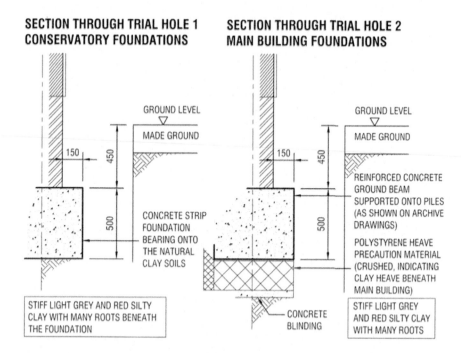

PRECISE LEVEL MONITORING RESULTS

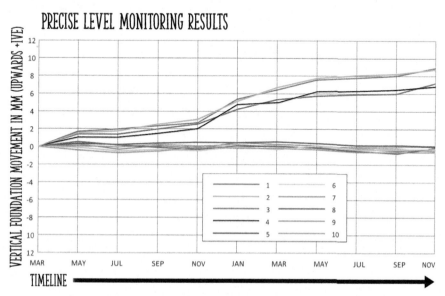

CRACK MONITORING RESULTS

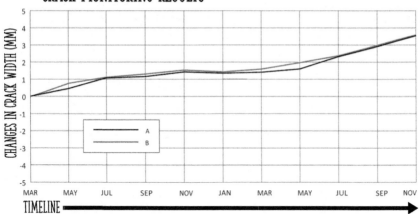

TIMELINE ➤

CF5.4.1 FORENSIC ASSESSMENT AT INVESTIGATION STAGE

FOUNDATION TYPE/DETAILS Two trial holes were excavated. Trial hole 1 revealed a concrete foundation projecting 150mm from the external face of the wall. The top of the concrete was located at 450mm below ground level (BGL) and the concrete thickness was 500mm. The underside of the foundation was located at 950mm BGL. Trial hole 2 revealed a concrete foundation projecting 150mm from the external face of the wall. The top of the concrete was located at 450mm BGL and the concrete thickness was 500mm. Clay heave precaution material had been installed beneath the foundation in trial hole 2, which confirmed that the main building had been constructed using reinforced ground beams spanning between and supported onto piled foundations.

The heave precaution material had crushed, indicating heaving clay soils (moving in an upwards direction) beneath the ground beams.

BOREHOLE INVESTIGATION DETAILS Two boreholes were carried out. One in the area of damage and one away from the area of damage (control borehole). The boreholes were taken to depths of 12m & 15m BGL.

SUBSOIL DETAILS

The trial holes identified made ground overlying stiff light grey and red silty clay with many roots.

Borehole 1 in the area of damage comprised: Topsoil to 200mm below ground level (BGL) overlying stiff light grey and red silty clay becoming very stiff from 2m BGL (gradually increasing in strength with depth) and with roots recorded to 4m BGL. The borehole was terminated at 15m BGL.

Borehole 2 away from the area of damage comprised: Made ground to 250mm overlying firm damp light grey and red silty clay becoming stiff from 2.50m and increasing in strength with depth. The borehole terminated at 12m BGL and a fixed datum was installed (which was used for precise level monitoring). SEE BD13.3.5

PLASTICITY INDEX (SOIL TESTING RESULTS)

A series of Atterberg limit laboratory tests were carried out on selected samples which indicated the liquid limit (LL) was in the range of LL=75 to 85 and the plasticity index (PI) values were recorded in the range PI=45 to 50, confirming the soil to be of very high plasticity. NHBC Standards Chapter 4.2 classifies the soil as having high-volume change potential (HVCP).

TREE ROOT ANALYSIS

Tree root analysis was carried out on a tree root recovered from beneath foundation in trial hole 1 (in the area of damage). The root was confirmed as being from an oak tree, which is classified as having a high-water demand in accordance with NHBC Standards Chapter 4.2. The desk study identified that an oak tree had been removed from the rear garden shortly after the conservatory was constructed.

DESSICATION ASSESSMENT

A soil desiccation assessment was carried out which comprised:

- Soil strength profile plots (as measured by pocket penetrometer).
- Soil moisture profile plots.
- Moisture content in comparison with Atterberg limit test results.

Assessment of the data indicates that the clay in the area of damage is desiccated to a depth of approximately 4m BGL, relative to soils away from the area of damage. Heave calculations were carried out using the data obtained from the control borehole and the borehole in the area of damage using the water content profile method. Hypothetical clay heave movements of up to approx. 70mm were predicted. See BRE Digest 412 for further reading.

MONITORING (RESULTS TO DATE)

The monitoring exercise indicates that the crack widths are increasing and there is a general trend of upward movement to the conservatory structure.

CF5.5 **THE TRIAL** DISCUSSION, CONCLUSIONS & RECOMMENDATIONS

Q. Has sufficient investigation work been undertaken to gain enough evidence to determine the cause of the damage?
'Yes, at this stage it is considered that sufficient information has been obtained to identify the cause of the damage.'

Q. Is further investigation required to provide evidence? 'No.'

Q. Is the damage due to ground movement?
'Yes, foundation movement caused by the effects of clay heave:

- Shrinkable clay soils were found beneath concrete foundations.
- A high-water demand oak tree has been removed prior to construction of the conservatory.
- Oak tree roots were found in the area of damage beneath the existing foundation.

- The laboratory analysis indicates that the soils were desiccated beneath the foundations, in the area of damage.
- The main building has been constructed onto piled foundations with heave precaution materials.'

Q. Is there evidence of progressive movement?

'Yes, the monitoring results indicate ongoing progressive movement in an upward direction.'

CF5.5.1 **THE VERDICT** CONCLUSIONS

An initial assessment, desk study and intrusive site investigation has been carried out.

The level survey, crack pattern of damage and further investigation, indicates foundation movement caused by the effects of clay heave (upward movement).

A large oak tree (located in the rear garden) was removed shortly after the conservatory was constructed. The tree roots travelled beneath the conservatory footprint, causing desiccation of the clay soils.

The source of desiccation was removed when the tree was cut down, which resulted in an increase in water content of the clay soil causing the clay to heave (move in an upward direction) as it returns back to its natural state.

Soil swelling caused by tree removal (particularly high-water demand trees in very high shrinkable clay soils) can be considerable and movements can continue for many years following removal.

Assessment of the ground conditions indicate significant desiccation up to 4m below ground level with a theoretical heave potential of up to approximately 70mm.

CF5.5.2 TIME TO PUT IT RIGHT RECOMMENDATIONS

OPTION 1. DO NOTHING This is not recommended as a long term solution as movement and damage is expected to get worse, due to the residual desiccation and clay heave potential.

OPTION 2. FURTHER MONITORING This option could be considered to check stability over a longer period. However, clay heave predictions are excessive, the clay soil could take a long time to stabilise and the building damage is now severe and will require reconstruction.

OPTION 3. VEGETATION CONTROL This is not an option, as the foundation movement is attributed to an oak tree removed prior to construction. There is a remaining oak tree in the rear garden however, this tree is located on the boundary line far enough away from the area of damage, not to influence the soils beneath the conservatory footprint and its pruning or removal will not improve the situation.

OPTION 4. UNDERPINNING Piled raft type underpinning could be considered however, it is not recommended on this occasion as a suitable repair solution on its own. The superstructure damage is significant and will require a complete reconstruction to correct distortions.

OPTION 5. COMPLETE RECONSTRUCTION ONTO NEW FOUNDATIONS (RECOMMENDED)

This option comprises: Carefully taking down the conservatory superstructure, setting aside suitable material for re-use, removing the existing foundations and reconstruction of the conservatory onto new piled raft foundations. The borehole investigation and soils analysis previously carried out were taken to a sufficient depth to provide pile design parameters.

THIS WAY FOR OPTION 3

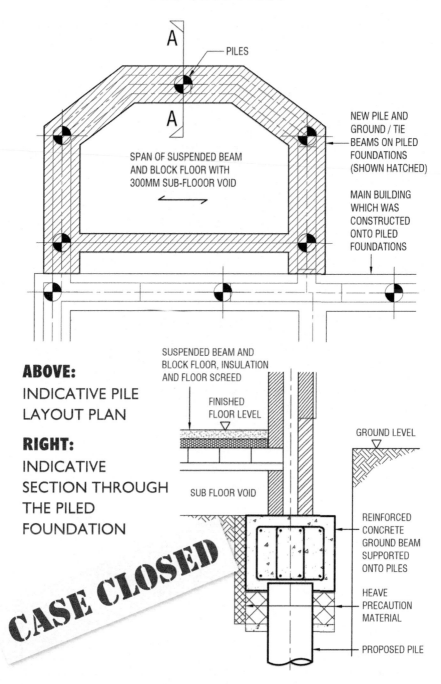

PILES

A

A

SPAN OF SUSPENDED BEAM
AND BLOCK FLOOR WITH
300MM SUB-FLOOOR VOID

NEW PILE AND
GROUND / TIE
BEAMS ON PILED
FOUNDATIONS
(SHOWN HATCHED)

MAIN BUILDING
WHICH WAS
CONSTRUCTED
ONTO PILED
FOUNDATIONS

ABOVE:

INDICATIVE PILE
LAYOUT PLAN

RIGHT:

INDICATIVE
SECTION THROUGH
THE PILED
FOUNDATION

SUSPENDED BEAM AND
BLOCK FLOOR, INSULATION
AND FLOOR SCREED

FINISHED
FLOOR LEVEL

GROUND LEVEL

SUB FLOOR VOID

REINFORCED
CONCRETE
GROUND BEAM
SUPPORTED
ONTO PILES

HEAVE
PRECAUTION
MATERIAL

PROPOSED PILE

CASE CLOSED

CF6 THE CASE OF THE HIGH-LEVEL CRACKS

CF6.1 **DESK WORK**
PROFILING THE POTENTIAL SUSPECTS

Previous section reference numbers A1, A2, B1, B2, ETC... included for further reading.

PROPERTY ADDRESS: Farm Lane

WITNESS STATEMENT: The property is a detached two storey building (rectangular footprint in plan) with a hipped tiled roof. Damage has been reported to the first floor internal walls at all four corners.

A1   Historic aerial photographs indicate trees surrounding the property boundary and a small stream in the rear garden.

A1   The site hazard report indicates that any clay soils on site are not likely to pose a significant risk. No other significant hazards noted.

A2   The building construction comprises masonry cavity walls with intermediate timber floors and a timber hipped raised collar tie roof.

A5   The British Geological Survey website indicates the potential for gravel and sandy ground conditions.

A6   There is no obvious risk of mining or landslip.

A7   The property was constructed approximately 11 years ago.

A8   The property is located in a rural location.

TIME TO VISIT THE CRIME SCENE...

CF6.2 **THE CRIME SCENE** THE SEARCH FOR CLUES

A9   The inspection was carried out in the summer months after a prolonged period of inclement weather.

A10   The property is in an elevated position on a site which slopes down from the back to the front.

A11   Trees surround the property (outside of the boundary).

A12   The underground drainage system is located to the front and side of the property.

A13   Similarly constructed properties in the area with no obvious visible external defects noted.

CF6.2.1 **WITNESS INTERROGATION**

Q. When was the damage first noticed?

'Cracks were noted soon after construction.'

Q. Have repairs been carried out to the area of damage?

'Yes, previous crack repairs were carried out.'

Q. Is the damage getting progressively worse?

'Yes, cracks have reappeared through the previous repairs indicating that the damage may be getting progressively worse.'

Q. Has the property been altered or extended?

'Not in the area of the damage.'

CF6.2.2 **INSPECTION** OF THE **BUILDING**

BD2   The area of damage is located internally to the first-floor perimeter external walls. The roof construction comprises a raised collar tie hipped roof with the wall finishes extending up the sloping sides of the roof (referred to as the skilling).

Vertical cracks were noted at the internal corners at first floor level. The top of the external cavity wall is bowing in an outward direction.

BD5 3mm wide cracks were measured which have re-appeared through previous repairs. This type of crack is likely to have some structural significance.

CRACK DAMAGE AND DISTORTION SURVEY

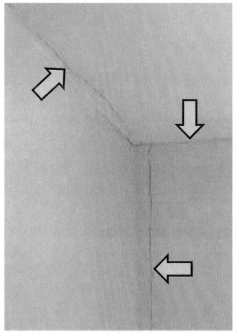
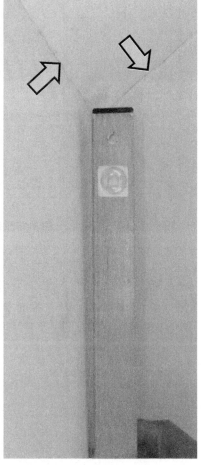

'PHOTOGRAPH ABOVE SHOWING CRACKING AT THE FIRST-FLOOR CORNER WALL JUNCTION. THE CRACK HAS REAPPEARED THROUGH A PREVIOUS REPAIR.'

'PHOTOGRAPH RIGHT SHOWING A SPIRIT LEVEL PLACED AGAINST THE TOP OF THE WALL INDICATING THAT THE WALL HAS MOVED IN AN OUTWARD DIRECTION.'

FIRST FLOOR LAYOUT PLAN

SHOWING THE ROOF STRUCTURE

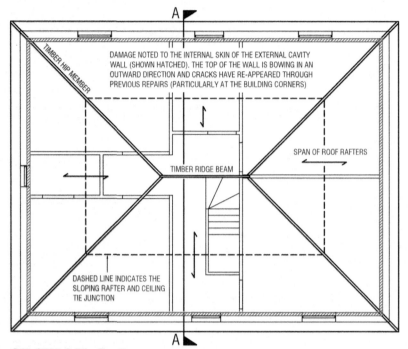

A

TIMBER HIP MEMBER

DAMAGE NOTED TO THE INTERNAL SKIN OF THE EXTERNAL CAVITY WALL (SHOWN HATCHED). THE TOP OF THE WALL IS BOWING IN AN OUTWARD DIRECTION AND CRACKS HAVE RE-APPEARED THROUGH PREVIOUS REPAIRS (PARTICULARLY AT THE BUILDING CORNERS)

SPAN OF ROOF RAFTERS

TIMBER RIDGE BEAM

DASHED LINE INDICATES THE SLOPING RAFTER AND CEILING TIE JUNCTION

A

SECTION A-A THROUGH THE ROOF STRUCTURE

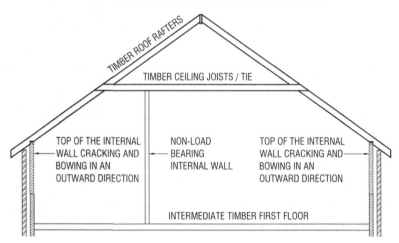

TIMBER ROOF RAFTERS

TIMBER CEILING JOISTS / TIE

TOP OF THE INTERNAL WALL CRACKING AND BOWING IN AN OUTWARD DIRECTION

NON-LOAD BEARING INTERNAL WALL

TOP OF THE INTERNAL WALL CRACKING AND BOWING IN AN OUTWARD DIRECTION

INTERMEDIATE TIMBER FIRST FLOOR

CF6.3 DE-BRIEF AT INITIAL SITE VISIT

COMMENTS & PRELIMINARY CONCLUSIONS:

An initial assessment, site survey and desk study has been carried out.

The structural arrangement of the roof construction and high-level crack pattern of damage, suggests the design of the roof structure may be inadequate. The roof could be spreading, resulting in an outward thrust at eaves level, where the roof structure is supported onto the inner skin of the masonry cavity wall.   SEE BD1

ADDITIONAL SURVEY WORK?

A distortion survey was carried out using a spirit level, which is considered sufficient to determine the direction and extent of movement.   SEE BD13.3.2

INTRUSIVE INVESTIGATION?

Further evidence is required to determine the cause of the damage.

The building finishes should be removed to determine the as-built construction details (size of structural members including their arrangement and the rafter and ceiling tie connection detail).

Once the as-built construction details have been confirmed, specialist structural calculations can be prepared to determine the theorical deflection and strength of the roof structure.   SEE BD2

CRACK MONITORING?

Crack monitoring is not required at this stage as monitoring is unlikely to influence the outcome of any remedial work which may be required.   SEE BD13.3.5

CF6.4 INTRUSIVE INVESTIGATION THE AUTOPSY

'PHOTOGRAPH LEFT SHOWING EXTERNAL ROOF FINISHES REMOVED REVEALING THAT THE RAFTER IS BOLTED TO THE RAISED CEILING TIE.'

SIMPLIFIED STICK AND PIN DIAGRAM BELOW INDICATING THE DEFLECTED SHAPE OF THE LOADED ROOF STRUCTURE (AS DETERMINED BY SPECIALIST STRUCTURAL CALCULATION).

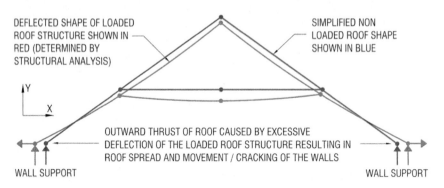

DEFLECTED SHAPE OF LOADED ROOF STRUCTURE SHOWN IN RED (DETERMINED BY STRUCTURAL ANALYSIS)

SIMPLIFIED NON LOADED ROOF SHAPE SHOWN IN BLUE

OUTWARD THRUST OF ROOF CAUSED BY EXCESSIVE DEFLECTION OF THE LOADED ROOF STRUCTURE RESULTING IN ROOF SPREAD AND MOVEMENT / CRACKING OF THE WALLS

WALL SUPPORT

WALL SUPPORT

CF6.4.1 FORENSIC ASSESSMENT AT INVESTIGATION STAGE

Intrusive investigations have been carried out to determine the as-built construction details, including the timber member sizes, arrangement and connection details. This site obtained as-built information was used to carry out theoretical structural calculations.

The calculations identified excessive deflection of the timber roof structure, which has resulted in an excessive outward thrust at the roof support position (where the truss is bearing and supported onto the top of the inner skin of the external cavity wall construction).

Several different load cases were considered in the structural analysis calculations comprising dead loading (self-weight) and imposed temporary loading (maintenance, wind and snow).

CF6.5 THE TRIAL DISCUSSION, CONCLUSIONS & RECOMMENDATIONS

Q. Has sufficient investigation work been undertaken to gain enough evidence to determine the cause of the damage? 'Yes.'

Q. Is further investigation required to provide further evidence? 'No.'

Q. Is the damage due to ground movement? 'No.'

Q. Is there evidence of progressive movement? 'Yes, it is likely that the damage could become progressively worse. Cracks have appeared through previous repairs and the structural calculations indicate excessive deflection of the loaded roof structure.'

CF6.5.1 THE VERDICT CONCLUSIONS

An initial assessment, desk study, intrusive site investigation and specialist structural design calculations have been carried out.

The structural calculations and pattern of damage comprising cracking and movement at the roof support position, indicates that the roof is spreading at this location due to inadequate design of the roof structure.

OPTIONS

CF6.5.2 **TIME TO PUT IT RIGHT** RECOMMENDATIONS

OPTION 1. DO NOTHING

It is likely that the damage could become progressively worse as the loaded roof structure continues to deflect and move.

OPTION 2. CARRY OUT ROOF STRENGTHENING WORK (RECOMMENDED)

One way to strengthen the roof would be to introduce new steel beams supported onto posts (hidden in walls) to vertically support the roof structure. Some of the new beams may need to be cranked so that they can safely transfer the roof loads (through adequate load paths) back to the loadbearing walls which will spread the loads down to the foundation level (see indicative roof section below).

TIMBER ROOF RAFTERS

A

TIMBER CEILING JOISTS / TIE

B

C

BY PROVIDING A VERTICAL SUPPORT AT POSITIONS A OR B & C, THE HORIZONTAL THRUST (LOAD) AT THE SUPPORT POSITION WILL BE REMOVED

CASE CLOSED

CF7 THE CASE OF THE DIAGONAL WALL CRACKS (PART 2)

CF7.1 DESK WORK
PROFILING THE POTENTIAL SUSPECTS

Previous section reference numbers A1, A2, B1, B2, ETC... included for further reading.

PROPERTY ADDRESS: Waterworks Lane

WITNESS STATEMENT: *Diagonal cracks have been reported on the rear corner wall of a detached two storey property.*

A1   Historic aerial photographs indicate that the previous site history comprised a large garden area and gravel driveway. No significant trees or vegetation were noted close to the building structure. Open fields are located to the rear.

A1   The site hazard report indicates that any clay soils on site are likely to pose a probable risk and volume change potential would be anticipated as being high. No other significant hazards noted.

A2   Archive construction drawings indicate that the building has been constructed using a load bearing timber frame structure, externally clad with brickwork, intermediate timber floors, a timber hipped roof and with a suspended beam/block ground floor.

A5   The British Geological Survey website indicates the potential for clay, silt and sandy ground conditions.

A6   There is no obvious risk of mining or landslip.

A7   The building was constructed approximately 15 years ago.

A8   The property is located on the outskirts of a built-up area.

TIME TO VISIT THE CRIME SCENE...

CF7.2 **THE CRIME SCENE** THE SEARCH FOR CLUES

A9   The inspection was carried out on a dry sunny spring day.

A10   The site is generally level around the building perimeter sloping up towards the rear.

A11   Low level bushes and shrubs are located along the rear boundary line, with an open field behind the boundary line.

A12   The main underground drainage system is located around the perimeter of the building, with a manhole cover located adjacent to the area of damage.

A13   No external defects were observed to similarly constructed neighbouring properties in the area.

CF7.2.1 **WITNESS INTERROGATION**

Q. When was the damage first noticed?

'The damage was first noticed approximately six months ago by a neighbour and could have existed prior to this date.'

Q. Have repairs been carried out to the area of damage?

'No, the cracks have not been repaired and appear to be getting progressively worse.'

Q. Have improvements been carried out to external garden areas? 'Yes, garden landscaping work was carried out which included the planting of shrubs, paths, retaining walls and steps.'

Q. Any other relevant information? 'During periods of heavy rainfall, a significant amount of surface water runs off the fields behind the property (which are at a higher level), flowing over the garden and waterlogging the gravel border located adjacent to the rear left corner of the building, in the area of damage.'

CF7.2.2 INSPECTION OF THE BUILDING

B4 The area of damage is located to the rear left corner travelling around the side and rear elevations.

Tapering diagonal cracks travel from the bottom corner of the first floor rear bedroom window, around the corner of the building and down the side elevation. The cracks continue down beneath the damp proof course (DPC) level on the side elevation.

The brickwork has moved out of plumb at the crack location on the corner of the building and at the DPC level, by approximately 5mm.

Internal vertical cracks were noted above and below the first-floor bedroom window.

BD5 The cracks were estimated as being up to 5mm wide. They are likely to have some structural significance and are likely to have been caused by ground movements.

CRACK DAMAGE AND DISTORTION SURVEY

CRACKING AND DISPLACEMENT OF THE EXTERNAL BRICKWORK WALL

CRACKS IN A DIAGONAL PATTERN

LAYOUT PLAN (SHOWING AREA OF DAMAGE)

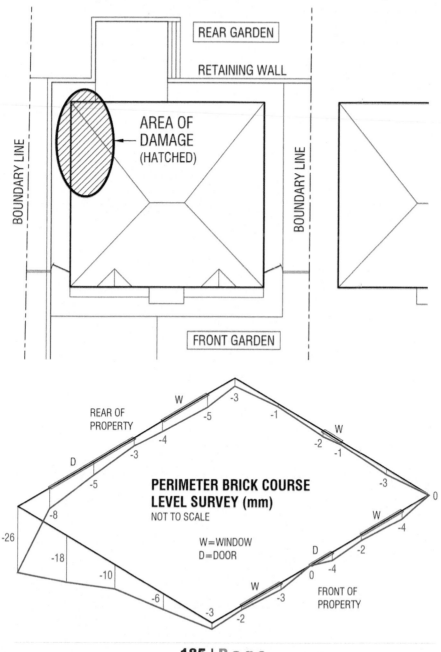

REAR GARDEN

RETAINING WALL

AREA OF
DAMAGE
(HATCHED)

BOUNDARY LINE

BOUNDARY LINE

FRONT GARDEN

REAR OF
PROPERTY

W   -3
    -5   -1
  -4
-3   W
D   -2
  -5   -1

  -8   -3   0

**PERIMETER BRICK COURSE
LEVEL SURVEY (mm)**
NOT TO SCALE

W=WINDOW
D=DOOR

W
            -4

-26
            D   -2
  -18   0 -4

    -10

        W
      -3   FRONT OF
  -6   -2   PROPERTY
    -3

BUILDING ELEVATIONS

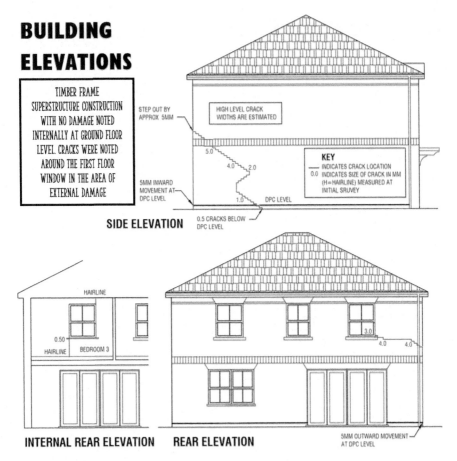

TIMBER FRAME SUPERSTRUCTURE CONSTRUCTION WITH NO DAMAGE NOTED INTERNALLY AT GROUND FLOOR LEVEL. CRACKS WERE NOTED AROUND THE FIRST FLOOR WINDOW IN THE AREA OF EXTERNAL DAMAGE

STEP OUT BY APPROX 5MM

HIGH LEVEL CRACK WIDTHS ARE ESTIMATED

5.0

4.0 2.0

5MM INWARD MOVEMENT AT DPC LEVEL

KEY
— INDICATES CRACK LOCATION
0.0 INDICATES SIZE OF CRACK IN MM (H=HAIRLINE) MEASURED AT INITIAL SRUVEY

1.0 DPC LEVEL

SIDE ELEVATION 0.5 CRACKS BELOW DPC LEVEL

HAIRLINE

0.50

HAIRLINE BEDROOM 3

3.0

4.0 4.0

INTERNAL REAR ELEVATION **REAR ELEVATION**

5MM OUTWARD MOVEMENT AT DPC LEVEL

CF7.3 DE-BRIEF AT INITIAL SITE VISIT

COMMENTS & PRELIMINARY CONCLUSIONS

An initial assessment, site survey record and desk study has been carried out. The crack pattern of damage suggests that it is likely that the building has suffered foundation subsidence (downward movement). Several factors could have attributed to the damage and further investigation is recommended to determine the cause of damage. SEE BD13 & 13.3.2

IS ADDITIONAL SURVEY WORK REQUIRED? Both the crack and brick course level survey provide sufficient evidence to determine the direction and extent of movement to the building. **SEE BD13.3.2**

DRAINAGE TEST OR SURVEY? A CCTV survey is required to inspect the condition of the underground drainage system, particularly in the area of damage. **SEE BD13.3.3**

INTRUSIVE INVESTIGATION? Hand dug trial pits are required to inspect the foundation construction and soils beneath. An area of cracked brickwork wall to be removed to inspect the wall construction details. **SEE BD13.3.4**

TREE REPORT OR ROOT ANALYSIS? Not required, as no significant existing or removed trees or vegetation in the area of damage. **SEE BD14**

ADDITIONAL INFORMATION Depending on the outcome of the initial investigation it may be necessary to carry out further investigation, in the form of boreholes, crack monitoring and precise levelling.

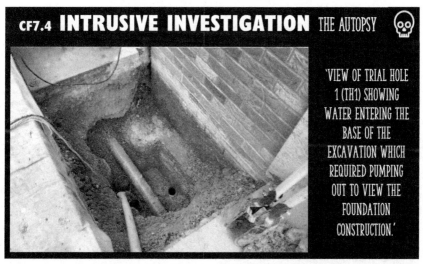

CF7.4 INTRUSIVE INVESTIGATION THE AUTOPSY

'VIEW OF TRIAL HOLE 1 (TH1) SHOWING WATER ENTERING THE BASE OF THE EXCAVATION WHICH REQUIRED PUMPING OUT TO VIEW THE FOUNDATION CONSTRUCTION.'

SEE OVER FOR TRIAL HOLE LOCATIONS ➡

TRIAL HOLE LAYOUT PLAN

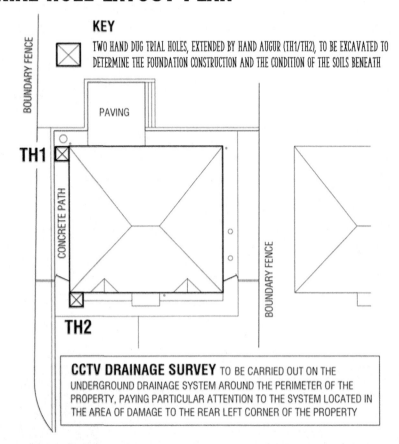

KEY

TWO HAND DUG TRIAL HOLES, EXTENDED BY HAND AUGUR (TH1/TH2), TO BE EXCAVATED TO DETERMINE THE FOUNDATION CONSTRUCTION AND THE CONDITION OF THE SOILS BENEATH

BOUNDARY FENCE

PAVING

TH1

CONCRETE PATH

BOUNDARY FENCE

TH2

CCTV DRAINAGE SURVEY TO BE CARRIED OUT ON THE UNDERGROUND DRAINAGE SYSTEM AROUND THE PERIMETER OF THE PROPERTY, PAYING PARTICULAR ATTENTION TO THE SYSTEM LOCATED IN THE AREA OF DAMAGE TO THE REAR LEFT CORNER OF THE PROPERTY

'VIEW OF TRIAL HOLE 2 (TH2) SHOWING FIRM CLAY SOILS (NO GROUNDWATER).'

'BRICKS REMOVED SHOWING THE INTERNAL TIMBER FRAME AND WALL TIES.'

TRIAL HOLE FOUNDATION DETAILS

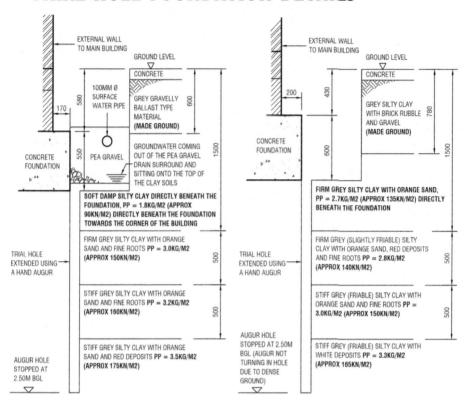

SECTION THROUGH TRIAL HOLE 1 (TH1)   SECTION THROUGH TRIAL HOLE 2 (TH2)

CF7.4.1 FORENSIC ASSESSMENT AT INVESTIGATION STAGE

FOUNDATION TYPE/DETAILS

Trial hole 1 in the area of damage revealed concrete strip foundations. The depth to the top of the concrete foundations from ground level was 580mm, projecting 170mm away from the face of the building. The concrete thickness was 550mm and the formation level was 1.13m below ground level.

Trial hole 2 (located away from the area of damage) revealed concrete strip foundations. The depth to the top of the concrete foundations, from ground level was 430mm, projecting 200mm away from the face of the building. The concrete thickness was 600mm and the formation level was 1.13m below ground level.

SUBSOIL DETAILS

Trial hole 1 (located in the area of the damage) was extended by hand augur, which revealed soft damp silty clay soils beneath the foundation, quickly becoming firm at around 1.50m. The clay soils increased in strength with depth. A surface water underground drainage pipe and manhole (surrounded by pea gravel) were located close to the foundation. Ground water was flowing out of the pea gravel and waterlogging the trial hole. A pump was used to remove the water so that the foundation construction details could be viewed. The pea gravel was approximately 100mm above the underside of the foundation.

Trial hole 2 (located away from the area of damage) was extended by hand augur and revealed firm silty clays beneath the foundation which increased in strength with depth to where it was difficult to extract soil samples (due to dense soils). No groundwater was encountered in this trial hole.

Soil strengths were measured using a hand penetrometer.

OTHER INVESTIGATION

A section of cracked loose bricks were removed at high level revealing the wall construction which comprised a cavity wall with an internal loadbearing timber frame and outer brickwork skin.

Wall ties had been installed at the appropriate centres in accordance with current regulations.

The ties were steeply sloping downwards to the outer skin and pulling out of the brickwork mortar joints, adjacent to the area of cracking.

DRAINAGE SURVEY

An underground CCTV drainage survey was carried out, which identified a defect with the underground pipe connection to the manhole. The pipe had dislodged and was leaking water into the pea gravel surround.

DRAINAGE LAYOUT PLAN (REAR CORNER)

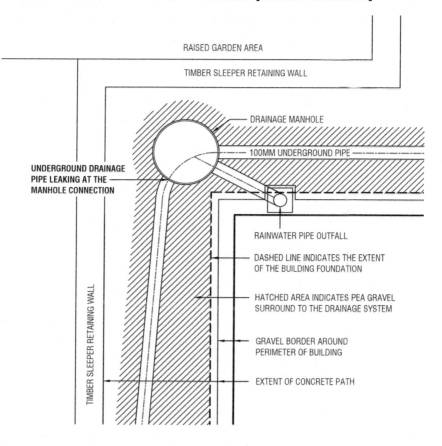

RAISED GARDEN AREA

TIMBER SLEEPER RETAINING WALL

DRAINAGE MANHOLE

100MM UNDERGROUND PIPE

UNDERGROUND DRAINAGE PIPE LEAKING AT THE MANHOLE CONNECTION

RAINWATER PIPE OUTFALL

DASHED LINE INDICATES THE EXTENT OF THE BUILDING FOUNDATION

HATCHED AREA INDICATES PEA GRAVEL SURROUND TO THE DRAINAGE SYSTEM

GRAVEL BORDER AROUND PERIMETER OF BUILDING

EXTENT OF CONCRETE PATH

TIMBER SLEEPER RETAINING WALL

CF7.5 **THE TRIAL** DISCUSSION, CONCLUSIONS & RECOMMENDATIONS

Q. Has sufficient investigation work been undertaken to gain enough evidence to determine the cause of the damage? 'Yes.'

Q. Is further investigation required? 'No.'

Q. Is the damage due to ground movement? 'Yes, foundation subsidence, due to softening of the clay soils beneath foundations:

✓ Trial hole 1 in the area of damage revealed groundwater flowing through and potentially remaining in the pea gravel surrounding the underground drainage system. The formation level of the pea gravel was close to the underside of the foundation.

✓ The clay soil located beneath the foundation on the rear left corner in the area of damage was soft and damp when compared to the clay soil located beneath the foundation away from the damage.

✓ The underground CCTV drainage survey identified that the surface water system travels around the rear left corner of the building where a manhole has been constructed at the change in pipe direction. The pipe connection is leaking at the manhole junction, which has probably been happening for a long period, due to poor workmanship at the time of construction.'

CF7.5.1 **THE VERDICT** CONCLUSIONS

An initial assessment, desk study and intrusive site investigation has been carried out. The crack pattern of damage and further investigation indicates that the rear corner of the building has suffered foundation subsidence (downward ground movement beneath foundations). This was caused by the effect of softening of the clay soil due to excessive surface/ground water collecting and potentially remaining in the pea gravel, which surrounds the underground surface water system.

CF7.5.2 TIME TO PUT IT RIGHT RECOMMENDATIONS

OPTION 1. DO NOTHING

It is probable that the damage could become progressively worse.

OPTION 2. CARRY OUT COSMETIC REPAIRS FOR AESTHETIC REASONS, NO OTHER ACTION

It is likely that any cosmetic repairs will be damaged in the short term, due to progressive movement.

OPTION 3. PERMANENTLY RE-ROUTE THE UNDERGROUND DRAINAGE SYSTEM

This option comprises completely removing the existing underground surface water drainage system for a distance of approximately 3m (or more) either side of the rear right corner and re-routing away from the building. Crack and level monitoring could then be carried out for a minimum period of 12 months to see if the clay soils beneath the foundation dry out and either stabilise or recover back to their natural state. If the damage does not become progressively worse (determined by monitoring) the superstructure could be repaired. However, there is a risk that the damage may become worse due to groundwater continuing to soften the clay soils (percolating through the disturbed ground) and the foundations may ultimately have to be underpinned.

The disadvantage of this option is that it would be difficult to achieve as there is not a lot of external space available to re-route the drainage, which would probably involve demolishing and reconstructing retaining walls and deep excavations, to form new manholes in the raised garden area at the change in pipe direction. This option does not remove groundwater and there is a risk that the clay soils will continue to soften beneath foundation level causing progressive movement, unnecessary cost and delay.

THIS WAY FOR OPTION 4

OPTION 4. TRADITIONAL UNDERPINNING TO THE REAR LEFT CORNER (RECOMMENDED)

This is the preferred option, and the work would involve the following:

Carry out traditional concrete foundation underpinning to the rear corner of the building, in sections to a depth of approximately 2m below ground level bearing into the firm/stiff natural soil, below the influence of ground water and the underground drainage system.

The underpinning should step up either side of the corner for a distance of approximately 3m on the rear and side elevations (6m in total).

The existing foundations have been constructed at a min depth of 1m below ground level and the ground conditions are consistent across the site (silty clay) so future differential foundation movement (caused by foundations bearing onto different soils types at different levels) would not be expected.

To facilitate the underpinning work, the existing surface water drainage system would need to be temporary rerouted and reinstated in the same location as before (with any leaks repaired).

On completion of the underpinning work, there will be no delay in carrying out the superstructure repair, which will involve partial reconstruction to the outer brickwork skin and installation of masonry reinforcement bars to strengthen the repair area.

'PHOTOGRAPHS ON NEXT PAGE SHOW THE VARIOUS STAGES OF THE TRADITIONAL CONCRETE UNDERPINNING, WHEREBY EXCAVATIONS ARE HAND DUG BENEATH THE EXISTING FOUNDATION IN CAREFULLY PLANNED STAGES DOWN TO SUITABLE GROUND CONDITIONS AND THEN BACKFILLED WITH CONCRETE.'

CF8 THE CASE OF THE OF THE WIDESPREAD CRACKING

FILE OPEN

CF8.1 DESK WORK
PROFILING THE POTENTIAL SUSPECTS

Previous section reference numbers A1, A2, B1, B2, ETC... included for further reading.

PROPERTY ADDRESS: Sandy Lane

WITNESS STATEMENT: Widespread cracking has been reported to the external walls of a detached bungalow.

A1   Historic aerial photographs show that the property has occupied the site since around 1960.

A1   The site hazard report indicates that any clay soils on site are not likely to pose a significant risk. No other significant hazards noted.

A2   Archive drawings indicate that the building was constructed with masonry cavity walls supporting a timber hipped roof.

A5   The British Geological Survey website indicates the potential for sandy/gravelly ground conditions and local knowledge of the area can confirm this.

A6   There is no obvious risk of mining or landslip.

A7   The property was constructed approximately 60 years ago.

A8   The property is located in a rural location.

CF8.2 THE CRIME SCENE THE SEARCH FOR CLUES

A9   The inspection was carried out on a dry and very windy summers day.

A10   The property is located onto a generally level site.

A11   Shrubs and trees are located to the left side boundary.

A12   The drainage system is located around the perimeter of the main building.

A13   No external defects were observed to the neighbouring bungalows in the area which had been built using different wall construction materials.

CF8.2.1 WITNESS INTERROGATION

Q. When was the damage first noticed?

'External cracks have always been present during occupation.'

Q. Have repairs been carried out to the area of damage?

'Yes, external crack repairs have been carried out and cracks have reappeared through the repair, although they do not appear to be getting progressively worse.'

Q. Has the property been altered or extended? 'No.'

Q. Any other relevant information? 'The external cracks appear to open and close depending on the time of year. The cracks on the south facing elevation are more noticeable during the summer months.'

CF8.2.2 INSPECTION OF THE BUILDING

B4
B5
B6
Widespread external wall cacks were noted travelling in a generally vertical direction through the mortar joints and cracking the larger blocks. The cracks are uniform in width over the length of the crack and do not pass through the damp proof course. The cracks are located centrally along the building elevations and around the window/door openings. The cracks appear to be old, with cobwebs in the larger cracks and with dirty smoothed edges.

The external cracks have appeared above and below the window/door openings and centrally along the wall elevations. The property measures approximately 10m long x 8m wide and has been constructed using masonry cavity walls with a concrete blockwork inner skin and with an artificial stone (concrete block) outer skin. Masonry movement joints were not visible. No corresponding internal cracking or damage.

BD5 The cracks were estimated as being up to 2mm (slight-moderate fine cracks which are easy to see when approaching 2mm in width). Cracks may have some structural significance but not usually serious.

CRACK DAMAGE AND DISTORTION SURVEY

'PHOTOGRAPHS ABOVE AND LEFT SHOWING THE FRONT AND SIDE ELEVATIONS OF THE BUNGALOW.'

SEE OVER FOR TYPICAL CRACK PATTERNS AND A PERIMETER BRICK COURSE LEVEL SURVEY

VERTICAL CRACKS WHICH ARE GENERALLY UNIFORM IN WIDTH OVER THE LENGTH OF THE CRACK AND DO NOT TRAVEL BELOW DPC LEVEL

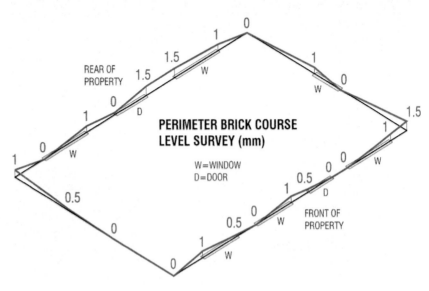

PERIMETER BRICK COURSE LEVEL SURVEY (mm)

W=WINDOW
D=DOOR

REAR OF PROPERTY

FRONT OF PROPERTY

CF8.3 DE-BRIEF AT INITIAL SITE VISIT

COMMENTS & PRELIMINARY CONCLUSIONS

An initial assessment, site survey and desk study has been carried out. The pattern and location of damage indicates that the cause could be attributed to thermal/moisture movement of the concrete blocks (at this stage). **SEE BD7**

IS ADDITIONAL SURVEY WORK REQUIRED?

The crack and brick course level survey are sufficient to determine the likely cause of the cracking. There is no need to carry out any further survey work (at this stage). **SEE BD13.3.2**

DRAINAGE TEST /SURVEY

A CCTV drainage survey is recommended to determine the condition of the underground surface and foul water system. This should be carried out to eliminate the potential for leaks, possibly washing out sandy/gravelly soils beneath foundation level, particularly as the drainage system appears to be old and there are tree roots nearby which could be entering and damaging the pipes. **SEE BD13.3.3**

INTRUSIVE INVESTIGATION?

Further intrusive investigation is not considered necessary at this stage. **SEE BD13.3.4**

CRACK MONITORING?

Yes, crack/level monitoring over a 12 month period (every 8 weeks). The results will provide additional evidence to verify the suspected cause. **SEE BD13.3.5**

TREE REPORT/ ROOT ANALYSIS?

Not considered necessary at this stage as it is unlikely that tree roots are influencing the damage. **SEE BD14**

CF8.4 FORENSIC ASSESSMENT AT INVESTIGATION STAGE

DRAINAGE SURVEY A underground CCTV drainage survey was carried out which identified clay pipework with some minor defects noted, mainly due to old age. Roots have found their way into the pipework through the old brick manholes (reducing the size of the pipes). In some areas the pipes were no longer level, allowing water to hold in areas of the pipework. No significant leaks were identified.

MONITORING (RESULTS TO DATE) The cracks are not becoming progressively worse with only minor movements recorded, indicating a cyclical movement trend (see indicative results below).

PRECISE LEVEL MONITORING (CARRIED OUT AROUND THE BUILDING PERIMETER)

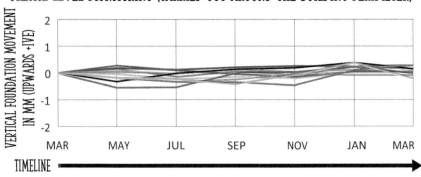

CRACK MONITORING (SELECTION OF CRACKS LOCATED AROUND THE BUILDING)

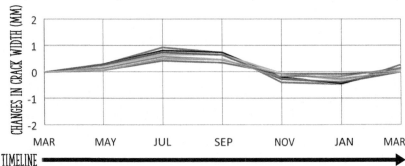

CF8.5 **THE TRIAL** DISCUSSION, CONCLUSIONS & RECOMMENDATIONS

Q. Has sufficient investigation work been undertaken to gain enough evidence to determine the cause of the damage?
'Yes.'

Q. Is further investigation required to provide further evidence? 'No'.

Q. Is the damage due to ground movement? 'No'.

Q. Is there evidence of progressive movement? 'The damage is irreversible and it is likely that the cracks could become progressively worse due to weathering and deterioration with age.'

CF8.5.1 **THE VERDICT** CONCLUSIONS

An initial assessment, desk study and further investigation comprising a CCTV drainage survey and crack monitoring has been carried out.

The pattern of damage and further investigation indicates that the cracks in the outer skin of the masonry cavity walls have been caused by thermal and moisture movements. Cracks are opening and closing on a cyclical basis as the different building materials move, expand and contract, when exposed to temperature and/or moisture variations.

No allowance has been made for this type of movement, which usually comprises the installation of movement joints.

As a general guide these movement joints should be positioned at 6m intervals for concrete blocks.

OPTIONS

CF8.5.2 **TIME TO PUT IT RIGHT** RECOMMENDATIONS

OPTION 1. DO NOTHING

It is likely that the damage could become progressively worse due to general weathering and deterioration with age.

OPTION 2. CARRY OUT REMEDIAL REPAIR WORK (RECOMMENDED)

Movement joints should be constructed in the outer skin of the cavity wall, in accordance with published guidance.

The new movement joints to be located in an area of vertical cracking and in an area which will not detrimentally affect the structural integrity of the building and/or aesthetics of the building structure. Sometimes it is possible to hide movement joints behind downpipes, provided they are not too close to the corners of the building.

Cracks in mortar joints should be re-pointed and broken blocks should be replaced. Brick reinforcement should be incorporated to strengthen the repair area.

Repairs to be carried out to the underground drainage system as recommended in the CCTV drainage survey report, comprising root cutting, partial re-lining and manhole repair.

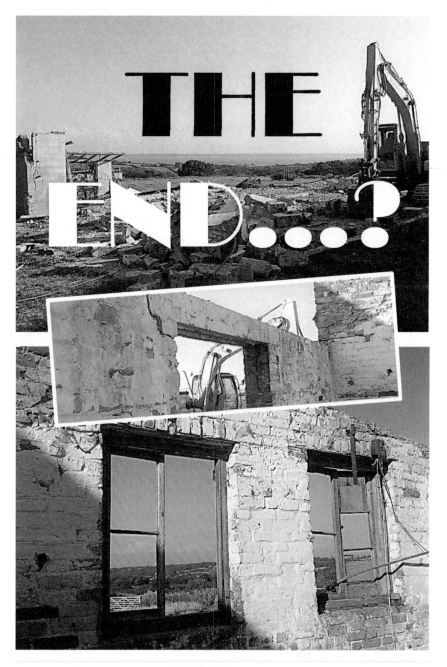

Sources

BRE Publications
www.brebookshop.com

BRE Digests
Good Building Guides and Good Repair Guides

Institute of Structural Engineers
www.istructe.org.uk

Subsidence of low-rise buildings, second edition
A guide for professionals and property owners

Surveys and inspections of buildings and associated structures

Building Regulations
Part A Structure – HMSO

NHBC - National House Building Council Standards

TRADA - Timber Research and Development Association
Wood information sheet

Surveys of timber framed houses

Index (FOR CASE FILES REFER TO THE SUMMARY AT THE END OF THIS INDEX.)

Case File Summary (THE ANSWERS)

CF1 The case of the cracking porch structure

Foundation subsidence (downward ground movement beneath foundations) due to the foundations being constructed onto made/ infilled ground which has settled/degraded over a period of time.

CF2 The case of the leaning retaining wall

Retaining wall failure due to an inadequately designed wall stem which is not strong enough to provide support to the retained ground.

CF3 The case of the diagonal wall cracks

Foundation subsidence (downward ground movement beneath foundations) caused by the effects of clay shrinkage due to existing tree root action.

CF4 The case of the ceiling stain

Wet rot damage caused by water penetration through the waterproof finishes on the second-floor roof terrace.

CF5 The case of the moving conservatory

Foundation movement caused by the effects of clay heave (upward movement) due to tree removal shortly after construction.

CF6 The case of the high-level cracks

Roof spread caused by the inadequate design of the roof structure.

CF7 The case of the diagonal wall cracks (Part 2)

Foundation subsidence (downward ground movement beneath foundations) caused by the effect of softening of the clay soil due to excessive surface, ground water and a leaking drainage pipe.

CF8 The case of the widespread cracking

Thermal and moisture cracking effects to the outer skin of a masonry cavity wall (not foundation related damage).

Printed in Great Britain
by Amazon

47567969R00119